WESTWARD MOVEMENT

BUFFALO BILL, *Stevenson*
DANIEL BOONE, *Stevenson*
DAVY CROCKETT, *Parks*
JESSIE FREMONT, *Wagoner*
JED SMITH, *Burt*
JIM BOWIE, *Winders*
JIM BRIDGER, *Winders*
KIT CARSON, *Stevenson*
LOTTA CRABTREE, *Place*
MERIWETHER LEWIS, *Bebenroth*
NARCISSA WHITMAN, *Warner*
SACAGAWEA, *Seymour*
SAM HOUSTON, *Stevenson*
TECUMSEH, *Stevenson*
WILL CLARK, *Wilkie*
WILLIAM HENRY HARRISON,
   Peckham
ZEB PIKE, *Stevenson*

THE NATION DIVIDED

ABE LINCOLN, *Stevenson*
BEDFORD FORREST, *Parks*
CLARA BARTON, *Stevenson*
DAVID FARRAGUT, *Long*
HARRIET BEECHER STOWE,
   Widdemer
JEB STUART, *Winders*
JULIA WARD HOWE, *Wagoner*
MARY TODD LINCOLN, *Wilkie*
RAPHAEL SEMMES, *Snow*
ROBERT E. LEE, *Monsell*
TOM JACKSON, *Monsell*
U. S. GRANT, *Stevenson*

RECONSTRUCTION and EXPANSION

ALECK BELL, *Widdemer*
BOOKER T. WASHINGTON,
   Stevenson
JOHN WANAMAKER, *Burt*

TOM EDISON, *Guthridge*

TURN of the CENTURY

ANNIE OAKLEY, *Wilson*
DAN BEARD, *Mason*
GEORGE CARVER, *Stevenson*
GEORGE DEWEY, *Long*
GEORGE EASTMAN, *Henry*
JAMES WHITCOMB RILEY, *Mitchell*
JANE ADDAMS, *Wagoner*
JOHN PHILIP SOUSA, *Weil*
JULIETTE LOW, *Higgins*
KATE DOUGLAS WIGGIN, *Mason*
THE RINGLING BROTHERS, *Burt*
ROBERT PEARY, *Clark*
TEDDY ROOSEVELT, *Parks*
WALTER REED, *Higgins*
WILBUR AND ORVILLE WRIGHT,
   Stevenson
WILL AND CHARLIE MAYO,
   Hammontree

IN RECENT YEARS

AMELIA EARHART, *Howe*
A. P. GIANNINI, *Hammontree*
BABE RUTH, *Van Riper*
ERNIE PYLE, *Wilson*
FRANKLIN ROOSEVELT, *Weil*
HENRY FORD, *Aird-Ruddiman*
JIM THORPE, *Van Riper*
KNUTE ROCKNE, *Van Riper*
LOU GEHRIG, *Van Riper*
RICHARD BYRD, *Van Riper*
WILL ROGERS, *Van Riper*
WOODROW WILSON, *Monsell*

Pocahontas

Brave Girl

Illustrated by William Moyer

Pocahontas

Brave Girl

By Flora Warren Seymour

THE **BOBBS-MERRILL** COMPANY, INC.
A SUBSIDIARY OF HOWARD W. SAMS & CO., INC.
Publishers • INDIANAPOLIS • NEW YORK

To a Gallant Little Indian Girl

Illustrations

Numerous smaller illustrations

Contents

Books by Flora Warren Seymour

POCAHONTAS: BRAVE GIRL
SACAGAWEA: BIRD GIRL

★ ★ Pocahontas

Brave Girl

Playful Girl
Hears a Story

PLOP-PLOP! Nantaqua, a young Indian warrior whose name meant Brave Son, was striding along in the woods. Suddenly he felt something hit him on the shoulder from above. He stopped short. Up and down, all around him, he looked intently. His hand clasped the bow which hung from his shoulder.

He did not reach for an arrow in the quiver by his side. He did not really fear any enemy, for he was near his home village. Here his father Powhatan was chief.

What could have hit him?

He could see no sign in the branches of the

pines above him or in the branches of other trees, whose leaves were turning to yellow and red.

His sharp ears caught the sound of water in the distance. There was a wide, deep river not very many miles away.

Plop-plop!

Nantaqua, after looking all around, had started off. Again there was a quick little blow on his shoulder. This time he could see what had hit him. Off he darted to the right. Up in the branches he caught a glimpse of brown.

"Come down here, you young rascal!" Brave Son called out with a laugh.

A laugh from above answered him.

Brave Son took hold of the tree and began to shake it briskly.

"Open your mouth, Nantaqua, and I'll drop something into it," called out a gentle voice from the branches above.

"No, you don't!" replied Nantaqua. "I know

12

very well we have had no hard frost yet, and this persimmon is bitter and tough. Pucker up your own mouth with it."

Another laugh answered him. An Indian girl about ten years old slipped down and stood beside him. She was his younger sister Pocahontas, Playful Girl.

"Well," said Nantaqua, pretending to be quite horrified. "No wonder our father calls you his play girl! What do you think you are—a young warrior? And why are you so far from home, Pocahontas?"

"I came out to watch for you, Nantaqua," said his sister. "I wanted to look for persimmons, too, but they aren't ripe yet. Neither are the chinquapins. They are still all locked up tight in their prickly little nests."

"Too early yet," said her brother. "That was a hard one you gave me."

He rubbed his shoulder as if it had hurt him.

Pocahontas knew from his smile that he was joking. "I hope you have something good to eat at home," he went on.

"Lots of good things," his sister answered. "The men came in this morning with a great pile of oysters. All the women are making bread from sunflower seeds. The beans are good, and there are fish from the river."

"That sounds fine to a hungry traveler," said Brave Son.

"Tell me all about your adventures, Nantaqua," begged Pocahontas.

"Later on I will tell you," said her brother. "I have been far to the south. They tell many strange stories of white-faced people from across the water. I have brought you something that one of them left behind." He tapped the deerskin bag that hung by his side.

His sister's eyes shone. She wanted to ask for the gift that very minute, but she knew that if she teased, her brother would be slower in giving it to her.

Swiftly and quietly they walked side by side to their Indian village home.

THE RING

The village in which they lived was on the banks of the river. About the bark-covered houses were the fields where the women planted corn and beans and tobacco.

The ripening corn was tall now. Among the uneven rows the pumpkins were growing big and yellow.

"I'll run ahead and tell them that you are coming," said Pocahontas.

They could see the small tree trunks set all around the houses for a stockade.

Nantaqua smiled as he watched her go. This youngest sister of his was the pet of the whole

15

village. Even Powhatan, the Head Chief, their stern old father, was gentle with her. She had no fear of him, though her grown-up warrior brothers often felt afraid of his anger.

Pocahontas reached the opening used as a gate. She made her way to the large central house. This had been built by placing young trees close together for the walls. Overhead the branches had been woven closely together for a roof. There were several holes left in the roof so that the smoke from the fire could find its way out to the sky.

Not all of the smoke went out that way. A great deal of it stayed inside. Pocahontas coughed a little as she pushed aside the mat which hung over the opening.

On a long bench her father Powhatan was resting. As his daughter came up to him, he raised himself on one arm.

"What now, Playful Girl?" he asked.

"Nantaqua is coming! He will be here in a breath!" Pocahontas cried out excitedly.

"Good!" said her father. "Raw-hunt, tell the women to make food ready."

Raw-hunt rose quickly from where he had been sitting cross-legged before the fire. He was off in an instant.

Although he was a grown man, Raw-hunt was no taller than Pocahontas herself. He was too small to be a good hunter or warrior, but he was a quick and clever messenger. The chief kept him near and found him useful at all times.

At Raw-hunt's news the women went quickly to work to prepare a meal for Nantaqua.

Brave Boy found the village very busy. All the people were eager, though, to hear what he had seen in the weeks he had been away.

"Let me wait on him," Pocahontas begged.

The cook smilingly ladled out a great portion of stew upon a bark platter.

"Carry it steadily," she told the eager girl.

Pocahontas walked carefully and brought the platter of steaming food to Nantaqua without spilling a drop.

"M-m-m!" he exclaimed. "How good corn and beans from the field taste after all these days. Fish, too! Where I have been the streams are all too rocky for fish. Ah, this is good!"

"You have been to the western hills," said one of the elder aunts, who was standing near.

"Yes, and far to the south." He pulled up the bag that was still hanging from his belt. "Now, Sister, here is something for you."

Pocahontas had never seen anything quite like the thing he put into her hand. It was a round yellow ring, hard and shiny.

"Put it on your finger," her brother suggested.

The ring was much too big for her finger. If she let her hand fall by her side, the gold circlet would quickly slip off.

"I shall wear it on a woven string around my neck," she said. "See, Nantaqua! I have something else to go with it."

She showed her brother a pearl she had been holding in her hand.

"We-wau found this when he was opening oysters today. He just gave it to me. I shall put it on the string, too."

"When you are older," said the aunt, "you shall have a long string of pearls to wear about your neck. Perhaps you can put this one in the middle of them."

"What is it?" asked Pocahontas. "Where did it come from?"

"I got it from a man down near the island where we gather shells," her brother answered. "You remember, all of you, that we have heard many stories of the people with pale faces who came to that land."

His listeners nodded.

"The man who sold me this yellow thing said that one of the pale-faced women had worn it on her finger. He did not tell me how it came to be his."

"Did they kill all of the strange people with pale faces?"

"I do not know. No one has seen any of them for many, many moons."

"Some of them have come up our rivers, too," said the aunt whom Pocahontas called Aunt Kobas. "They have not left anyone behind them, though, as the people who came to Roanoke Island did."

Nantaqua was interested. "I would like to hear that story, too," he said.

The oldest aunt of all, Teemo, was not far away. "I can tell you that story," she said, "but you are too tired to hear it tonight. Have your good sleep and in the morning come to me and you shall hear all about it."

The next morning Pocahontas was so excited that she could hardly wait for Nantaqua to wake up. She was as eager as he to hear the story of the palefaces.

Aunt Teemo was up early too. She was sitting out in front of her house, braiding a mat of grasses. When Pocahontas came to her side Teemo began to braid and twist some of the grasses into a cord for the ring Brave Son had given his sister.

"Watch me and see how I do it," she told the excited girl. Pocahontas watched carefully. Aunt Teemo even let her braid and twist the strands a little, as she came near to the end.

"Let me have your yellow ring," Aunt Teemo said. She took it and fastened it carefully in the center of the cord, braiding it in so neatly that it would take a sharp eye to see where they were joined together. Then she hung it around the

22

girl's neck. "That," Teemo told her, "is the beginning of a necklace for you."

"Put the pearl on too," Pocahontas begged.

Aunt Teemo did so. "There really ought to be one on each side," she said.

"I shall ask We-wau for another when he has oyster shells to pry open," Pocahontas declared.

Pocahontas knew that almost anyone in the village would do favors for her. The old chief was very kind to her. She was his favorite daughter. Her own mother had died when she was a baby. As long as she could remember, all these aunts and elder sisters had looked after her and loved her. It was as though she had a whole village full of mothers.

Nearly everyone was a relative of some sort. The younger children were her cousins or the children of her grown-up sisters and brothers. She called them all cousin, for that was the way of the tribe.

Pocahontas felt proud of her beginning of a necklace. "See!" she cried as her brother came toward them. "I shall wear this always."

"How will you manage when you turn handsprings and stand on your head?" Nantaqua said, laughing. He knew how his sister loved to romp about and play.

Pocahontas hung her head a moment. "I suppose I shall have to take it off then, but I shall be careful not to lose it."

"Now, Aunt Teemo," said the young man, "we are waiting to hear all about those paleface visitors."

"From what people say," said Teemo, looking up from her work at the tall young warrior, "I think there are different kinds of palefaces—some darker than others."

"Yes, I have heard that too," said Nantaqua.

Pocahontas nodded, her black unbraided hair swinging loosely.

"Which kind of paleface came to our land?" Nantaqua continued.

"Both," said Aunt Teemo, "but the later ones with the lighter faces have sailed around in their boats and landed only long enough to get some water or wood. It is of the earlier, darker ones that I am going to tell you.

"The first ones came long, long ago. They did not stay, but when they went away they took with them a boy from one of our villages.

"Years later they came back, and the boy had grown to be a man. Such a man! He looked like the palefaces, except that he did not have hair on his face. He dressed like them, and talked their strange talk.

"He said they had taken him far across the salt water to a country called Spain. They had treated him well and given him all he could wish for. They had named him Don Luis.

"He had not entirely forgotten our way of talking, but at first he spoke in a way that sounded very queer."

"Did he stay here then?" asked Pocahontas.

"Oh, yes, but at first he did not stay with his own people. Some of the palefaces—he called them Spaniards—stayed for a while in a little village north of here. These men did not dress like our Don Luis. Instead, they wore long robes of black."

"What did Don Luis wear?"

"The strangest things—a hat with a feather in it, a jacket of heavy leather and long stockings that he pulled on over his feet and far up above his knees. That was while he stayed with the men in the black robes. When he came back to his own people he began to get rid of the new things, one by one. He let his hair grow long again and wore a band about his head. He began to like the feeling of air on his bare skin, as he had felt it when he was a boy.

"The Indians all listened to him, for he was a brother of their chief.

"They soon began to be angry with the men in the black robes. They would no longer give them food when they came to the village. Don Luis, also, was angry, and he let them start off hungry, too.

"As the black-robed men went away, the men of that tribe shot many arrows into the messengers. They killed all the Spaniards who were left. The medicine men sang all their chants over Don Luis, so that he would forget the strange things he had learned in Spain.

"There was one thing he remembered and taught our people. He said it was better for the villages whose language was the same to be friends. Because of what he told us, your father Powhatan is treated like a chief when he goes to other villages."

"Aunt Teemo, what became of Don Luis?"

asked Pocahontas. She was thrilled to think of this red man who had traveled among the pale-faced people across the great salt water. "I would like to do that," she thought to herself, "but I would not want to kill them if they came here."

"Well, all was fine with Don Luis that winter. In the spring the Spanish ships came back. Then he ran away to the south for fear they would punish him. He came down to our village. He brought some others from his village with him, and one of them, Pocahontas, was your very own mother."

Pocahontas was surprised and glad. Her own mother had seen and known the strange pale-faces. "Maybe I shall see them, too, someday," she thought.

She and her brother both thanked Aunt Teemo for telling them the story. Then Pocahontas went away, still thinking about those strange people with the white faces.

Pale-faced
Men Come

Frost came soon. The persimmons grew red and soft and sweet. The chinquapins burst right out of their horny burs. Pocahontas enjoyed hunting for them. One time she watched a busy squirrel and went carefully after him as he scampered away with a nut.

"I am a hunter, too," she thought, as she tracked him to the hollow log where he put his nut away. Then he went off for more.

Pocahontas felt inside the log and found more nuts than she could hold in both her hands. She was carrying a basket. She put all the nuts from the log into it.

"Thank you, squirrel," she said, laughing, "for gathering these for me." The squirrel would be disappointed, she knew, to find his hiding place empty. "There will be plenty more for him," she said to herself.

The children of the village had great fun eating nuts that afternoon.

The squirrel had been storing up food because he knew that winter would come soon. Winter made both a squirrel and an Indian want to stay under shelter most of the time. Pocahontas spent more days by the fire when the cold rains came.

Once in a while there was snow like a soft blanket over the whole land. Then Pocahontas could see rabbit tracks, tiny and round.

With a great shout the boys all went out to hunt. Pocahontas begged from Raw-hunt a bow and arrows he had been making. Though this was against the custom of the tribe, the chief's daughter had her way.

Pocahontas was very proud when she too came home with a rabbit. "I shall catch enough for a mantle, all fur and feathers," she told Aunt Kobas happily.

"You would do better to learn how to take care of this skin," her aunt told her.

For a good many of the winter days, then, she sat by the fire and made her rabbit skin ready for use, by pounding and drying it.

The short winter days went away quickly and pleasant weather came again. The women now were working at their fields for another season of planting. The seeds that had been stored away all winter were brought out and the women put them into the ground by hand.

Already the birds were back from the south. Pocahontas loved to hear their songs and to watch their bright wings flashing in and out.

No one liked to have the birds pick up the corn and beans that had been planted.

"We do not work like this just to feed those thieving creatures," Aunt Teemo said.

A wooden platform had been built out in the middle of the cornfield. Many of the villagers took turns watching there to frighten the birds away. Raw-hunt had a long stick with flapping streamers of grasses which he waved for a great distance around him. Pocahontas liked to sit near by. She thought it was fun to dart at the birds and scare them off.

"Why don't we stick poles like yours all around?" she asked Raw-hunt. "Then, when the wind blows the streamers, the birds will be frightened away."

"Maybe it would," he agreed. "We'll make some, anyway."

All that day when he was not waving his branches at the saucy crows, he sat making more streamers with the grasses and reeds that Poca-hontas gathered.

"There!" she said, when Raw-hunt had stuck several poles here and there in the field. "That will help to keep the birds away when they are too far for you to reach."

"Yes," he agreed. "At any rate, it will help until the leaves get too dry to flap any longer."

"By that time," Pocahontas suggested hopefully, "perhaps the corn will all be up."

"Maybe so," said Raw-hunt. "By that time, though, we shall all move down the river to where we find the fish."

"I remember last time," Pocahontas told him. "Perhaps when the white dogwood blossoms are waving on the trees."

"We shall see," Raw-hunt told her.

THE STORM

In their log canoes they made the journey down the river. Pocahontas wanted to paddle one of the canoes, but Brave Son persuaded her to wait until someday when he and she could go together without the others.

Pocahontas and the others were tired of sitting

still when the canoes were at last brought up to a wide sandy beach. A few minutes' walk through the woods—and there was the village looking much the same as when they had left it the summer before. There were fifteen or twenty houses, just like those they had left behind.

"Here's our house waiting for us," said Pocahontas happily.

"Not quite ready," said an older sister. "We shall have to bring bark and make mats for the roof. I can see too many holes where the water will come in when it rains."

"Who made the holes?" asked one of the younger cousins. He was a boy about three years old. His name was Chanco. He loved to follow Pocahontas around.

"It was Old Chief Wind and Old Chief Winter," the older sister told him. "They are great enemies of ours."

"I thought our enemies were the Susquehannoks," Chanco objected. His tongue stumbled a little over the long word.

"Some of our enemies are people and some are bigger things," the older sister said.

This remark made little Chanco look thoughtful. Later he asked Pocahontas what it meant.

"I think she means that the rain beats down on the roof and makes holes in it," Pocahontas told the boy, "and the cold weather and ice make things go crack, and the wind blows trees and our houses down."

"Then the storm is our enemy too."

"Yes, indeed," she answered. "It is a great enemy sometimes. I have seen it knock down some of our biggest trees."

It was not many days later that a big storm came upon them. The women were still working to repair their houses. The men were busy with the fishing nets. Clouds kept drifting across the sky and hiding the sun.

Then it grew very dark, and a great wind began to roar through the forest. The trees waved and twisted their branches around. The skies roared and sent down rain. Long, jagged streaks of light showed in the skies.

Chanco was frightened to hear the thunder and see the strange flashes of light.

He came up close to Pocahontas and took her hand. "Don't let it hurt me," he begged.

"It won't if you stay here," Pocahontas told him. She could remember that once she, too, had been afraid to hear the thunder. She and Chanco kept close to Raw-hunt, who was mending the knots in a fishing net.

"I am glad we are not out in our canoes," Raw-hunt told them. "You will see, tomorrow, that that water has come away up among the trees, and has then gone back again."

"How can we see if it goes back?" asked Chanco curiously.

"It will leave things behind it," Raw-hunt told him. "Leaves and branches and maybe even whole bushes."

WINGED CANOES

Sure enough, the next day was bright and sunny. Pocahontas and some of the other girls decided to go around exploring.

"I want to go too," said Chanco.

Pocahontas shook her head. He looked so disappointed that at last she nodded and said, "All right, come along."

"Now, Playful Girl," said Aunt Kobas, "if you take Chanco with you, be sure to watch out for him. Don't let him wander away from you—it would be very easy to lose him."

"I promise," said Pocahontas. Indeed, she meant to take the very best care of the child, for she was fond of him. Chanco liked her because she was more gentle and friendly with him than the other girls were.

"I don't see why you bother with him," said Fisher Girl, who was a friend of Pocahontas.

"Oh, he won't be any trouble," Playful Girl assured her.

Later on, however, in the woods leading down to the shore, the two girls started to play with some branches of a maple tree that had been uprooted by the storm. There lay the tree on its side, with its fresh green leaves all spread out flat. The girls pulled off some switches and began to chase each other over the slippery pine needles. Back and forth they went, laughing and calling out. It was a sort of tag game.

Pocahontas was a good runner. Fisher Girl was out of breath when she finally caught Pocahontas and touched her switch to her friend's shoulder. "Now it's your turn to run," said Pocahontas.

"Not just yet," said Fisher Girl. "I want to rest for a few minutes."

The two sat down side by side under a pine tree. Both were breathing hard from their chase. They watched a bluebird come out on a branch. They listened while he sang. They had almost forgotten their playmates.

"Where are the others?" Fisher Girl asked suddenly. "I can't hear them any more."

"Where is Chanco?" said Pocahontas, jumping up and looking around. "Oh, dear, I'm not looking after him as I promised! Aunt Kobas told me to watch him."

They rushed back to the place where they had left the other girls. No one was there.

"They must have gone down to the water," said Fisher Girl.

The two hurried along through the trees to the sand beyond. In the woods, before they reached the sand, they found the rest of the girls. They were busily digging under the dried leaves. "We are hunting for roots," they told the worried girls.

Pocahontas looked all around. "Where is little Chanco?"

"I thought he was with you," said one of the other girls.

"He was with us awhile ago," said another, "but he isn't here now."

No one had any idea where the three-year-old Chanco had gone.

Pocahontas' heart was beating with alarm now. She hurried on down the sand. Away over at the edge of the water was little Chanco, standing on a large rock. There was water flowing all around him, for the tide had turned and was now beginning to come in.

"Chanco!" Pocahontas cried as she came near him. "Come back!"

"It's all water!" he answered her in fright. "Where is the land?"

He stood there as if he did not know in which direction to jump.

"Wait for me, then," she called out.

Chanco stood still until she waded slowly out to the rock.

"Now lean down and put your arms around my neck," she told him, "and I'll carry you back to where it is dry."

Chanco did as she told him. He was heavy, and Pocahontas herself was not very big. Finally she managed to pull him and herself up the wet slippery beach to a drier place.

"Look!" Chanco cried excitedly, as they dropped down tiredly on the sand. He waved his hand toward the bay.

Pocahontas looked. Her first thought was that they must not be seen here. There were strange, large canoes.

She scrambled to her feet and seized Chanco by the hand. "We must get back among the trees, out of sight," she said, as they scurried back from the water's edge and into the woods.

From the shelter of the forest they watched the strange canoes, which at first had seemed far away. Now they came nearer. There were three of them—much bigger than any canoes Pocahontas had ever seen. On top of them were tall poles, pointing to the sky.

From these poles floated great white things that looked like enormous wings. When the wind puffed, these wings blew out round and fat.

Pocahontas could not see anyone paddling, but there were men moving around the poles. They were too far away for her to tell what they really looked like or what they were doing.

Slowly, quietly, the strange, winged canoes moved on. Playful Girl turned to Chanco and took him by the hand.

"It looks like magic to me," she said. "We must hurry home to tell my father about this."

Though Pocahontas and Chanco hurried back, they found that another messenger had arrived before them. This was Opekankano, Chief Powhatan's brother.

Opekankano was the strongest and most warlike of the uncles of Pocahontas. It was he who led the parties of warriors that went out to fight their enemies. The people of the villages called him Opekankano because that meant Fierce War Chief. Head Chief Powhatan was their leader in time of peace.

When Opekankano entered the house where his brother Powhatan was sitting, he scarcely noticed that Pocahontas slipped under his arm. The two reached Powhatan at the same time. It was the warrior who spoke.

"Strange news." He stopped for a moment. "In the big storm we were near where the two points of land show the way to the great salt

44

water. While we struggled to bring our canoes up the bank, we saw a strange sight.

"In the thick of the storm were three great canoes with wings. They were like the ones we heard of—that came long ago, bringing the pale-faced people. We could not see the men—they were but specks as the waves tumbled their big boats along. The canoes kept on into our bay. So we came back to tell the people."

"We saw them too," Pocahontas spoke up. She had been listening to all her uncle had said, so quietly that the two men had not noticed her. "We saw them—Chanco and I."

"Where?" asked her uncle.

"Tell us about it, child," her father bade her.

"We went down through the trees to the beach—a lot of us girls. I had promised to watch Chanco, but while I was playing he ran off down to the water. I had to go get him. He saw the white-winged canoes and pointed to them.

"I could not see the people very plainly. They just looked small in the distance. Sometimes light flashed back when the sunlight shone on them. They kept on going up the river, and we ran back here to tell you."

"It must be palefaces," said Fierce War Chief.

"You have done well," said Powhatan to his daughter. "Now find Raw-hunt for me."

Pocahontas found Raw-hunt at work on his nets. She told him her story.

"Raw-hunt, do you think they were pale-faced men?" she asked.

"They must be. Our people have no such winged canoes as those." He folded up his net carefully. "Someone else will have to finish this work," he went on. "I see that it will be my part to go from one village to another to tell the people about the palefaces."

"Won't you take me along with you?" Pocahontas cried.

Raw-hunt smiled, looking at her eager face. "You can scarcely go fast enough. I shall run most of the way."

"I can run, too," she insisted.

Raw-hunt laughed. "You can be busy helping us to move back up the river. Since the canoes have gone that way, I think your father will want to return."

"Oh, yes—here is something We-wau found for you this morning." He put another pearl into her hand.

Then Raw-hunt went off to Powhatan, very fast, as if to show Pocahontas how quickly he could go, even though his legs were quite short.

A Visit North

In the late summer Playful Girl went on a visit to the north. Here, on the river called the Potomac, was the village of her Uncle Japazaws and his wife.

Pocahontas liked to visit here. It was fun to turn handsprings on the flat sandy beach. She hunted for wild blackberries, juicy and sweet. She found the cattails in the smaller streams, and brought rushes to Aunt Jappy, to be used in making baskets.

A few miles up the river was a place where the water dashed over the rocks. Often Pocahontas played in the woods beside the stream. All about were smaller stones good for making arrowheads. The men would be busy chipping away at stones and forming them into points for their arrows.

Pocahontas liked to watch them.

"Do you really need so many arrows?" Pocahontas asked one of them.

"Other people need them too," the man told her. He was steadily chipping away at one stone with another.

"Do you give the arrowheads to other people?" Pocahontas went on.

"They give us many things for them," the busy arrow maker told her. "Skins, perhaps, or feathers to make into the robes which we wear when it is cold. They can use the arrows to shoot birds and beasts."

"Do you shoot them, too?"

"Sometimes. I can do this better, though, so I spend more time here, and let someone else do the hunting for me. That is a fair exchange, isn't it? That is why they have given me the name of Arrow Maker."

Pocahontas loved to sit by Arrow Maker and watch him bring the round stone to a point. Sometimes he chipped off a large piece, but more often only tiny flakes of white stone came away, until he had made it just the shape that would serve the hunter best. Arrow Maker very seldom spoiled one. He was careful to choose stones that did not have flaws in them.

Pocahontas often brought stones for him. She was learning to pick out for him the clear whole ones that would not break.

CAPTIVE BOY

"I have a playmate for you," said Aunt Jappy one day. "He does not talk much of our language now, but I think you will soon teach him."

"Is he an enemy?" Pocahontas had heard that

all those who spoke a different language from hers were enemies.

She looked with curiosity at the boy, who was nearly as tall as she. She smiled at him in a friendly manner.

"He *was* an enemy," her aunt told her. "Our warriors captured him. They would have killed him, too, but I chose to adopt him instead. I will take him in place of my own boy who was killed in fighting with the Mohawks. One day soon he will learn to call me Mother, and I shall call him Son."

"Did the men who captured him give him to you?" Pocahontas asked, still wondering how it had all happened.

"That is our custom," Aunt Jappy said. "If a woman wishes, she can save a captive—either a boy or a girl—by adopting him as her own."

"Can she adopt a man or a woman, too?" asked Playful Girl.

"Yes, a man or a woman, too," said her aunt. "We have a right to do this. It is the way of our people. Usually she chooses a young captive to bring up as her son."

Pocahontas was thinking this all over as she led Captive Boy away to show him where she liked to play.

Pocahontas enjoyed teaching Captive Boy to talk in her language. As they went along, she would tell him the word for leaf, or bush, or stone. The lad would repeat the word after her until he had the sound just right. They laughed together when a word seemed especially hard for him to learn.

"Walk," Pocahontas would say in her own language. Then she would show him what she meant by walking.

"Tree." She would say, pointing to a tree and he would then try to form the word which she had given to him.

It was not long before they were talking together quite easily.

Soon Captive Boy was helping Pocahontas to find good stones for Arrow Maker to use. Up and down the river the two would roam together. Pocahontas found it was much more fun when Captive Boy was with her.

"I think I'd like to adopt Captive Boy myself," she told Aunt Jappy.

Her aunt laughed. "He's my boy now. You will have to find another for yourself. Wait until your old uncle Fierce War Chief comes back with a captive.

"Besides, aren't you rather young to have someone to take care of?"

Pocahontas only smiled. She was thinking to herself, "I shall pick an older one, not one I have to take care of." She did not tell anyone about this, though.

"I have heard," her aunt went on, "that your

uncle has captured one of the pale-faced men that have been staying below here."

"Oh!" cried Pocahontas, "I saw their big canoes come into the river." She told Aunt Jappy all about the three vessels, while Captive Boy listened carefully.

When Playful Girl had finished her story, Aunt Jappy said, "Well, there were many strange-looking men in those great canoes. The first night they went on shore a band of warriors decided to attack."

"I know about that!" said Captive Boy. "My father and brother were there. They said they did not want any white-faced strangers in our country. They wanted to kill or capture all of the newcomers."

"Did they kill any?" Pocahontas asked.

"No, the strangers had left someone to watch. He saw our men coming near. He shouted to the others. They all jumped to their feet.

"My father was near enough to see each of them snatch up the long stick that he had at his side. They held these sticks up with their hands and pointed them at our people.

"Out of each stick came a great noise and a big puff of smoke. Then little round balls came flying out. When one of them hit a man he would fall down to the ground. My father and brother and the other men ran away as fast as they could, so they would not be hit.

"My father says this is the most powerful magic he has ever seen."

"I have heard," said Aunt Jappy, "that the palefaces carry long shiny things, too, that are very sharp."

"Yes," said Captive Boy. "My father says these are great magic, too. They cut up everything they touch. They hurt worse than an arrow. They send out bright flashes of light when the sun shines on them."

"Why do we want to fight the strange-looking palefaces?" asked Playful Girl.

"I don't know why," said Captive Boy. "We just don't want strange people coming into our country, I suppose."

"It is the custom of our people, children," said Aunt Jappy.

A NIGHT ADVENTURE

Pocahontas had a big idea, but she did not speak of it when Aunt Jappy was with them. When she and Captive Boy had gone off to gather some dead branches for the fire, she told him what she had in mind.

"Wouldn't you like to see one of those pale-faced men?" she asked Captive Boy.

"Indeed I would," he told her. "That's what I was doing when your people caught me. I was trying to keep up with a party of warriors."

"Then come on," she said.

"Come on where?" asked the boy.

"Let's go find the palefaces now. If my uncle, Fierce War Chief, has captured one of them, we shall be able to find him. I can guess what my uncle is doing. If he doesn't kill a prisoner the first thing, he will take him around to a lot of villages and show him to the people. Then, last of all, he will go to the home village where my father is the Head Chief."

"All of those places are a long way off," objected Captive Boy. "I don't know the way to go to find them."

"I know the way to the nearest village," said Pocahontas. "I'm sure my uncle will come there. It is down this river a way, and then across through the woods to the next river. I want to go and see the pale-faced man."

"So do I," said Captive Boy, "but let's wait until it is nearly dark and then we can get away when no one sees us. Can you find your way there in the dark?"

"Oh, yes. I know I can," answered Pocahontas. "The first part is really very easy. We just go down the river."

That evening, after they had brought back the sticks for the fire and had helped to eat the succotash Aunt Jappy had made, they watched until everyone seemed to be asleep or resting. Then each went off in a different direction. In a few minutes they met by the white sands.

"I brought some dried deermeat," said Pocahontas, "so we shall have something to eat. It will be late tomorrow afternoon when we get there, even if we walk all night."

They soon found that they couldn't walk quite all night. They began to grow tired and sleepy.

"Oh! I shall have to rest awhile," Pocahontas said, with a great yawn.

"I tell you what," said Captive Boy. "You lie

down here and rest, and I'll sit and watch. Then, after a while, you can watch while I sleep."

"All right," said Pocahontas. She was so sleepy she could scarcely say even that. She cuddled down under some dried leaves at the foot of a tree and fell fast asleep.

Captive Boy sat down near by. He thought he could keep awake and watch, but his head drooped. Almost before he could look around, he too was sleeping.

It was the morning sun that wakened them. Captive Boy felt ashamed to think he had not been a good watchman, but Playful Girl just laughed at him.

"Nothing hurt us, anyway," she told him. "And now we can go right on to the village."

The sun was high up above them when they ate some dried deermeat and drank from the waters of a clear little stream. "We are not very far off now," Playful Girl told her companion.

Suddenly Captive Boy lifted his hand as if to tell her to be quiet. She looked around, but did not stir. Then a little sound came to them. It was the step of someone coming near—someone who was not looking for an enemy or hunting. He did not mind if he stepped on a twig or made a branch rustle.

"If he were stalking something," Pocahontas thought, "he would be so quiet I would not be able to hear a sound."

She and Captive Boy knew how to be quiet. Without a word, without disturbing a leaf or a twig, they drew back into the shade of the trees. They disappeared from sight. From behind the trees, though, two pairs of dark eyes were watching, and two pairs of keen ears listened intently.

Again they heard the sound. Someone was coming near to the place where they had been standing. Then, with a little cry, Pocahontas dashed out right in front of the traveler.

"Raw-hunt!" she cried.

It was indeed her father's messenger.

LOST BOY

Raw-hunt was astonished to see Pocahontas here in the forest, far from any village.

"How did you come here, Playful Girl? Where are you going?" he asked, in a voice full of anxiety. "Why are you in the woods alone and far from home?"

"I am not really alone," she told him. She turned back toward the trees. "Captive Boy!" she called. "Come out! This is a friend!"

There was no answer.

"He must be afraid of you," she told Raw-hunt. "He is Aunt Jappy's adopted boy, and we came down this way together. We heard that Uncle Fierce War Chief had captured a paleface and we thought we might get to see him. Tell me, is it really true that our warriors have a pale-faced man with them?"

"Indeed, it is true," Raw-hunt told her. "That is why I am going in this direction—to tell your uncle and aunt and the arrow makers."

"What is he like?" asked Playful Girl. "How soon are our men and he coming? Where are you going next?"

"Stop, stop!" said Raw-hunt. "How can I tell you so many things at one time? First you must tell me how long you have been away from your aunt's home. She must be worried."

His voice sounded troubled. Pocahontas hung her head a moment. She knew that her aunt would not have wanted her to go.

"We left just about dark," she told Raw-hunt, "and came down along the river until the moon was away up. Then, this morning we turned down this way. I have been here before—I knew the way. Captive Boy came with me."

Again she called him, and Raw-hunt joined in the call. No one answered.

"He is afraid, perhaps," said Raw-hunt, "or maybe he thinks he is near enough now to his own people to reach them. How old is he?"

"Not so old as I am," Pocahontas answered.

"Well, maybe he will get back to his tribe. What will your aunt say?"

Pocahontas looked very sober. "I—I don't know." She could guess, though, that her aunt would be sorry to lose the boy she had adopted. She would be very angry with Pocahontas for running away with him.

"Well, I think you will find out soon," Raw-hunt told her, "for that is the direction in which I am going. It will be best for you to go along with me, Playful Girl."

Pocahontas was very unwilling to go. She did not think it would be at all pleasant. She imagined she could hear her old friend Arrow Maker laughing at her—"Ho-ho! So you went out to see a captive and lost one instead." She did not like the idea at all.

"I think I'll go on where the warriors are," she told Raw-hunt.

"What will your Uncle Fierce War Chief say?" Raw-hunt asked her.

Pocahontas considered this. She was a little bit afraid of her warrior uncle. She knew he would not like the way she had left the village on the Potomac.

Perhaps it would be wiser not to let him see her for a while. He would be very cross over the disappearance of Captive Boy—perhaps even crosser than Aunt Jappy.

On the whole, it seemed better to go with Raw-hunt back to her uncle and aunt.

"All right," she said to Raw-hunt. "I'll go with you now."

"You will have to go fast," he told her.

"I'll run all the way," she promised.

Although Raw-hunt's legs were no longer than her own, she knew that he could move them very much faster.

He did not really make her run, of course, but she had to go very fast over the trail she and Captive Boy had followed. All the way she kept looking about for Captive Boy, but she saw no sign of him. Her heart grew heavier when they neared the village on the Potomac.

She felt quite sad when she saw how unhappy her aunt was about Captive Boy.

"He was to take the place of my lost son! Now I have lost my son once more." Aunt Jappy wept and pulled her long hair, all unbraided, down over her eyes.

Pocahontas was ashamed and she crept away out of sight. "I did not mean to make her so unhappy," she said to herself. "I know now, it was not a good thing to do."

Paleface
Wonders

Pocahontas came quietly back into the circle of the fire that evening.

"These men came out to trade with our people," Raw-hunt was saying.

"I think," he went on, "that they do not have any corn in the country they come from. They did not know, at first, how to use it. Now they like it very much. Also, they like the beans and pumpkins our women have dried for winter use."

"Do you think they mean to stay here?" asked one of the men.

"At first we thought they would go away. They brought no women or children with them. Their three big canoes sailed away, and a great many of the men stayed behind. When the summer days were long and hot many of them died. I think they were not used to so fierce a sun in their own country.

"Now they are going about trying to trade strange things they have for something to eat."

Raw-hunt drew a handful of bright objects from the pouch at his side. Pocahontas came up nearer to look at them.

"These shells they call beads. See the very little holes in them? See the many different colors? Now, here is something even more magical. They call it a looking glass. Look straight into it, Playful Girl."

He held something round and shiny in his hand. Pocahontas looked into it.

"There's a girl in it!" she cried in surprise.

Others crowded around to see.

"It's a man!" cried one of the warriors.

"No, it's a woman!" said Aunt Jappy, who stood beside Pocahontas.

Raw-hunt laughed gleefully. "When I look into it, I see Raw-hunt, the short man. Each one of you sees himself."

Pocahontas looked again, while Aunt Jappy stood aside and frowned at her. The Playful Girl she saw in the mirror was clearer than the image she had ever seen in the water.

In the glass she saw a brown-faced girl whose black hair hung down beside her smooth cheeks. The eyes were dark but shone back at her. Around her neck the woven string, with the little gold circle, hung down below her chin.

"When I am older," she thought, "I shall have a long string of pearls. My hair will be braided to hang down on each side. I shall have bright red paint on my face. I shall wear a cape of feathers. I wonder how long it will be till I can do all of these things."

She was not longing for this time to come. She knew that she would then have to give up playing and begin working all day with the women. It would be hard not to roam about and romp with the other girls.

"The pale-faced man has stranger magic than this," Raw-hunt was telling those around him. "First, it was something so surprising that Fierce War Chief did not kill this one man as he had killed the others."

"Why not? What was it?" Everyone was asking questions.

"It's something you hold in your hand," Raw-hunt told them. "It is like this glass, but when you look into it you do not see yourself. Instead, there is a thin shiny thing called a needle. You can't touch it—all you touch is the glass.

"Now listen carefully. That needle points toward the great star up in the sky that always stays to the north of us. No matter which way the pale-faced man turns his hand around, this needle turns too. It is very great magic.

"We all looked at it. We could not see how the needle got inside, nor how it could turn in there. Fierce War Chief is now taking him around to show it to all the villages."

"Ah! Ah!" A buzz of excitement went through the group.

"Now I have come to tell you that he will soon be on the way to Powhatan's own village. If you wish to see him and his magic needle, that is where you must go."

"We will go! We will go!" many voices answered him.

"I will go, too," said Aunt Jappy. "Playful Girl, you shall go with us. Perhaps you will not run away from there."

Ashamed, Pocahontas hung her head and made no answer.

"The pale-faced man has an even greater wonder," Raw-hunt went on. "If I had not seen this myself, I would never believe it."

"Ah! Ah!" came from the eager listeners.

"It is something he calls paper," Raw-hunt explained. "He tore it off of some which he took out of his great leather coat. Then he made dark scratching marks on it.

" 'Take this,' he said, 'to the people at our village, and they will give you the presents I have promised you.'

"Four or five of us took the paper. It was like the inside of the bark of the birch tree, only thinner and not so stiff. We went close up to the village of the pale-faced men, and then we were afraid. Finally we decided that if the paper could tell them about the presents, it would tell who we were.

"I crept up close to the walls and stuck this paper on a bush. Sure enough, they saw it. In a few minutes one of the men came out. He took it in his hand and looked at it carefully. He went back behind their walls.

"Soon others came out and called to us to come on and get the presents. That is the way I happen to have this glass.

"Truly the paper *could* talk. I do not see how it could. I did not hear it say anything. Maybe it talks only to pale-faced men."

Pocahontas listened in wonder. This was hard to believe and harder still to understand. "I hope someday I shall see the magic paper," she said to herself. "These people must be wonderful."

Thin white stuff that talked! All the men and women were wondering how it could possibly happen. Great magic, indeed!

"Now they will take him to Powhatan," Aunt Jappy was saying. "That will be the end of him and his magic."

Pocahontas felt a chill. Of course her father would have the pale-faced captive killed. All his

wonders would be lost. She wanted very much to
see this strange man.

THE RETURN HOME

"Take care of this girl and see that she doesn't
run off," Aunt Jappy said to Raw-hunt, as they
started off toward Powhatan's town. Aunt Jappy
could not forget the Captive Boy.

Pocahontas was glad to go alongside Raw-
hunt. She felt that he was her special friend and
would not frown at her.

Many were the questions Raw-hunt had to answer about the wonders he had seen and heard.
Pocahontas listened to everything.

"What do these people look like?" was the
question most often asked.

Again and again Raw-hunt made the same
answer. "Their hair is lighter than ours, sometimes quite yellow or even red, and more often

brown. Hardly more than one or two have black hair like ours. They do not let it get very long either. It grows thick on their lips and chin, so that they often look like wild animals.

"Most of them have light-colored eyes—something like the color of the sky. Their faces are a pale color, much lighter than ours."

"How do you know how they all look?" Pocahontas asked him.

"Oh, they have been watched from the very first," Raw-hunt told her. "I myself saw them many times. It is easy for us, who know the woods, to get near them without letting them hear and see anything. You are pretty good at that yourself." Raw-hunt laughed at the girl's surprised face.

"Yes, I have seen you often," he went on, "when you were stalking someone in the woods. Are you perhaps planning to become a warrior, Playful Girl?"

Pocahontas looked confused. "No, I suppose not. Anyway, I don't like to kill things—even little things. They look so unhappy! I only want to know what is happening all around."

"Indeed you do," said Raw-hunt. "Ever since you got out of your cradleboard I have been snatching you out of some trouble. Now, little Chanco follows me around as you did when you were his age."

"Oh, I shall be glad to see Chanco! Has he grown while I was away?"

"Oh, yes, he thinks he is old enough now to go with the other boys, but they don't agree with him. He'll be glad to see you."

This was in the cold season of the year. When they stopped for the sleeping time the fires felt good to Playful Girl. She was glad to snuggle under the skin blanket that kept Aunt Jappy warm for the night.

"They tell me the pale people have softer

blankets than ours, not so heavy and very warm," Aunt Jappy said. "They call them wool."

"I think I'd like them," said Pocahontas. "Skin blankets are so stiff and hard."

"You are always ready to try new things," said Aunt Jappy.

Playful Girl was thinking hard. "Aunt Jappy," she asked, "why don't you ask Father to let you adopt this strange pale-faced man? Then he could teach us all how to make the many wonderful new things."

Aunt Jappy shook her head. "It is a boy I want, Playful Girl. I would not know what to do with a man, and a strange one at that. I have lost my Captive Boy—the one who was to take the place of my own son."

Pocahontas felt the reproof in her aunt's voice.

When the crowd of travelers drew near the village of Powhatan, they saw Chanco standing by the gate, looking eagerly in their direction.

As soon as he caught sight of Pocahontas he rushed up to her.

"Oh!" he cried. "Playful Girl, I have been watching for you every day. The women are all preparing a big feast. We shall have great fun together again."

He reached up and put his arms around her neck. Pocahontas was glad to see her playmate again. Together they went about to see everything that was happening in the village.

The cooking fires were all burning brightly. Chanco and Playful Girl sniffed hungrily at the delicious smells that came from the pots.

Pocahontas' Bravery

ALL of the aunts were glad to see Playful Girl back again. Each one gave her and Chanco something to eat. By the time she had greeted them all, Playful Girl felt that she had been given a royal welcome and feast.

"More and more people are coming," they told her. "Everyone wants to have a look at the pale-faced prisoner before——"

"Before what?"

"Before your father tells the men with the clubs to get rid of him."

"Why are we going to do that?"

"It is our custom," the women answered her.

80

Pocahontas did not like such a cruel custom. Adopting was a much better plan, she felt sure.

She was thinking very seriously as they went to the big council hall.

Head Chief Powhatan was lying on a wide seat of wood, which was spread with skins and furs to make it comfortable. A crackling fire was burning in front of this couch.

At each end of the couch stood one of the younger aunts. Each had a sort of fan, made of feathers, which she used to keep the smoke away from the old Head Chief's eyes. No other girls or women could stand near him.

Standing all around were many warriors. Behind them were the women, craning their necks to see all that they could.

Pocahontas and Chanco could not see at all, because so many taller people were in the way.

Soon a stir around the door told them that the prisoner was being brought in. Pocahontas began to slip through the lines of grown people toward the front row.

The women looked at her frowningly. The men were too intent on watching what was happening to notice her very much. Besides, they knew her father would let her do things no other girl would dare try.

As she went by Raw-hunt she gave a little tug at his skin robe. He looked at her with a smile. "I almost believe he knows what I want to do," she thought.

A chorus of "Ah-h-h!" went through the crowd when Fierce War Chief and his men brought in the pale-faced captive. No pale-faced man had ever come so far inland.

This man was not very tall. He did not look fierce or cruel. His clothes and the color of his skin were strange indeed. The great brush of hair that spread around his chin especially made them exclaim with wonder.

"He says his name is John Smith."

"The other palefaces called him 'Captain' and did what he told them."

"His magic is very great, but it will not do him any good now."

These were some of the things Pocahontas heard as she made her way to the center of the crowd. Her father was watching the prisoner. He did not even notice when his daughter came near to his couch.

The aunts stood near by and fed the prisoner, but that did not take long.

Rain and snow had fallen on him as they had come along, and his clothes were wet and clammy and cold. He shivered a little and held out his hands toward the fire.

He did not look afraid, but turned his blue eyes on everything curiously. He looked at the Head Chief in his gayest deerskin mantle trimmed with pretty shells. He looked at the warriors, who scowled fiercely. He looked at the stone clubs of the men who stood nearest to him.

After the pale-faced prisoner had finished eating, Powhatan asked some questions. The prisoner tried to answer. With gestures he tried to make his meaning plain. He showed the Head Chief his glass with the imprisoned needle. He pointed up to the sky.

In the end Powhatan shook his head. The warriors growled impatiently. Powhatan gave a short command. Fierce War Chief repeated it in a loud voice.

Pocahontas knew what it meant when men came in with three great flat stones. Many times she had seen other captives forced to kneel before these huge stones.

Then the great clubs would be brought down on their heads, and they would speak no more. She could not bear to think of it. She pressed closer to her father's side.

"Father!" she called out. "Father! Do not let them kill him!"

Her girl's voice was not strong enough to be heard over the shouts of the warriors.

Her father was busy watching the men who were placing two of the flat stones side by side. Then the third, larger and heavier, was placed

on top of the two. Powhatan, seeing the men at their task, did not even hear her.

"Be quiet, child! This is a time for men to talk!" said the aunt who stood nearest her.

"Father!" She tugged at his deerskin mantle. "Do not let them kill him! I want to adopt him! Please, Father!"

Powhatan felt the tug at his mantle and glanced for a moment at his daughter. There were tears in her big dark eyes. She held out her imploring hands to him. Powhatan only frowned and looked back at the prisoner again.

Two stout warriors took Captain John Smith by the arms. Then they began to pull him toward the stones.

The pale-faced captain did not resist. He walked as proudly as if he were going by his own wish. When the warriors tried to push him down, he knelt easily. He laid his head on the stone, as they showed him.

The great fighting men now took up their clubs. At the end of each club was a heavy round stone of the sort found in streams. These were fastened with leather strips to stout sticks of oak.

The warriors raised their clubs. In a minute, Pocahontas knew, those awful stones would come down on the head of the prisoner. She could not bear it any longer.

Right under the lifted arm of one of the men she rushed. In a second she was beside the stones. She leaned over, quick as a flash, and put her own head on the head of the prisoner.

"No! No!" she cried. "I won't have him killed! I want to adopt him."

Struck by surprise, the warriors stopped still for a moment. Their clubs were held motionless high above her.

Then Head Chief Powhatan sat up straight at last. He saw that grave danger was threatening his own Playful Girl.

"What is this?" he called out. "What does this mean? Do not strike!"

The men lowered their clubs.

Pocahontas stood up. She could scarcely speak now. "He is my captive," she claimed, facing her father and looking into his stern eyes. "I want him for my own, as Aunt Jappy claimed her Captive Boy."

Her father looked at her a long time in silence. He could see how excited and eager she was.

"Very well," he said at last. "Since you wish it, his life will be spared. We shall adopt him as a member of our tribe."

A New Name
for Pocahontas

"Fisher Girl," said Pocahontas the next morning, "my father is going to adopt the pale-faced captain today."

"What is adopt?" asked Chanco, who was right at the elbows of the two girls.

"It means," Pocahontas explained, "that now he is going to belong to our tribe.

"I know a place," she added, "where we can peek in and see him."

"Let me go, too," begged Chanco, as the two girls started off.

"You must be very quiet if you go with us," they warned him.

Very carefully the three slipped around to the far side of the council house.

"There's the hole," said Playful Girl. She had to stand on tiptoe to look in.

"There he is!" whispered Fisher Girl, when she had looked in.

"Let me see, too," begged Chanco.

"I'll hold you up," said Pocahontas.

Fisher Girl had to help her.

Chanco looked in at the captain. "Why did you stop our warriors from hitting him?" he asked Playful Girl.

Pocahontas smiled. "I knew Father wouldn't let them hit me." She went on more seriously, "I don't like to see people get hurt, do you?"

"I don't know," said Fisher Girl.

"Yes!" shouted Chanco, and both girls held up their hands for him to be quiet. He added in a lower voice, "I like to hear the clubs go *whack, whack* on their heads."

"It hurts people and sometimes kills them. You wouldn't like them to do it to you!"

"If they are our enemies—" Fisher Girl began.

"If they said we were enemies, I suppose they would beat our heads, too," said Pocahontas. "I don't see why so many people have to be enemies anyway. We are going to promise not to be enemies to the palefaces. Then maybe—" her face lighted up as she thought of it—"maybe we can go and visit them at their village."

"Here comes someone," said Fisher Girl.

Pocahontas pulled herself up for her turn at the chink. She saw a tall warrior come hopping in at the door of the council house. He was painted black with streaks of red. On his head was a huge turban of fur, with otter and weasel tails hanging all around. His face was almost hidden. From his head, feathers stuck out in all directions.

"Here they are," said Playful Girl, as a great

band of black-painted warriors came trooping into the building. Soon they were dancing and leaping all around the captive.

It was a little quieter when Head Chief Powhatan came up to Captain Smith. Soon the pipe of peace was lighted and passed around the circle.

"Now I will call you my son," said the old chief. "You shall be one of us. You shall make drums and hatchets. And you shall make beads and bells for my Playful Girl."

"Just listen!" said Pocahontas very softly. "Come on, let's hurry around to the front, and be there when they come out."

A GROWN-UP PUPIL

"Bring me a basket," said Captain John Smith. Only at first he could not say all the words. One by one he learned them from Pocahontas, pointing to the basket to learn her word for it. Then he drew out the strange, magic thing Raw-hunt had told her about.

"Paper," she said, putting her hand upon it. She remembered what Raw-hunt had said.

"Yes, paper," he told her, showing her one thin sheet after another, "in a book."

Then he made black marks on it. "Po-ca-hon-tas." He repeated her name slowly as he made the marks.

"Does it talk?" she asked him. She put her ear up against it. "Raw-hunt said it spoke."

"It talks to me," he said, "and someday if you keep those bright eyes and ears of yours open, it will talk to you, too."

After many words back and forth, he had something to read her from the marks in the book. It had been like teaching Captive Boy. However, this grown-up captive seemed to learn very quickly. Perhaps there was indeed a great magic in this book, Playful Girl thought.

This is what he read to her: "Tell Pocahontas to bring me a little basket, and I will give her beads to make a chain."

Pocahontas laughed and held out her basket to him, to show him that he had said it all right. At once he gave her a handful of small, colored beads. How bright and shiny they looked! She gasped in surprise.

"For you," he told her.

She took from around her neck the string that held her golden circle and the two pearls. She untied the ends. Soon the two, the dark-eyed Indian girl and the yellow-bearded captain, were laughing together as they strung the beads on the woven cord.

Now there was a long stretch of beads on each side of the pearls. When Pocahontas tied them around her neck once more, she felt very fine and proud indeed.

She was proud when she showed them to

Fisher Girl and to Chanco. They admired her new ornaments very much.

"Maybe I can get some more for you, Fisher Girl," said Pocahontas.

"You see," she said to Chanco, "he is a kind man, and we ought to be good to him."

Chanco nodded.

"If my father calls Captain Smith his son," she went on, half to herself and half to the others, "I do not know whether he is my son, too—or my brother, perhaps."

"Why don't you ask him yourself?" suggested Fisher Girl.

"That is a very good idea, and I will do it!"

NONPAREIL

Captain Smith asked Pocahontas, "Weren't you afraid when the big clubs were held so closely over your head?"

"Oh, no," she answered quickly. "My father would never let them really hurt me."

"Lucky girl!" said the captain. "You are my friend. I owe you my life."

"I wanted to adopt you," said Playful Girl, "the way Aunt Jappy adopted Captive Boy. If my father has adopted you, though, I suppose you can't belong to me too."

Captain Smith's blue eyes twinkled. "Don't you think you are rather young to have a grown man for a son? I am old enough to be your father instead, Pocahontas."

"I suppose so," she said doubtfully. "I thought it would be nice, anyway."

She told him the story of Captive Boy and how she had helped him escape. "I hope he got back to his own people," she said at the end.

"I do, too," said the captain. "I hope to go back to my people, too. In a few days, I feel sure, your father will send me back to our village. We have things there that he would like to have, and perhaps he will trade some corn for them."

"I see," said Playful Girl. "If they go to your village I shall come along too."

"Please do," said Captain Smith, "and then we shall always know that those who come are friends and not enemies."

"Shall I say then that you are my son?" she persisted.

Captain Smith laughed. "I don't believe they would understand that. Suppose, when you come to our village, you call me your father instead. I have noticed that many of you say Father when you speak to the older men."

"My pale-faced father," said Pocahontas, turning over the words to see how they sounded. "All right. I like that. I shall know that we always belong to the same family, even if your face is pale."

"Indeed, you are right," said the captain. "As long as I live I shall never forget your kindness.

"I shall have a new name for you, too. I shall call you Nonpareil. In my language it means 'nothing equal.' It means that I have never seen a child so kind and so thoughtful."

"Nonpareil," Pocahontas repeated after him. "I think I like my new name. I have a secret name that we do not repeat—that was given to me when I was born. Then I have the name my father gave me—Pocahontas, Playful Girl. Now I have still another—Nonpareil."

FOOD TO JAMESTOWN

"B-r-r!" said Raw-hunt. "How cold it is!"

"I do not remember any winter so cold as this one," said Aunt Teemo.

"The palefaces are suffering in their village," said Raw-hunt.

Pocahontas listened.

Raw-hunt had just come back from the white

village. Powhatan had been willing to let the captain go back to his own people. With him he sent twelve men, who were to bring back two cannon and a stone for grinding meal.

"They were far too heavy for us," Raw-hunt admitted. "There stood the two big cannons. All twelve of us could not lift one of them and carry it, nor the millstone, either.

"At first we thought there was some trick or magic to it. We asked the captain to show us if they could really shoot like the smaller ones.

"They made such a terrible noise we all shouted with surprise. Out from the end of the big guns came the balls and flew off into the woods. The trees shook and bent over. It was a frightful sound."

"You could not bring them?" asked Nantaqua.

"Not the guns, nor the huge stone. Captain Smith sent us other presents, though. Some are especially for you, Playful Girl."

From his pouch Raw-hunt brought out more gay-colored beads and some red cloth to make into turbans.

Pocahontas came closer. He put into her hand a little mirror in which she could see the reflection of her own eager face. Then, last of all, he took from his pouch a string of little bells that tinkled merrily when he handed them to Pocahontas.

Pocahontas was happy indeed. Chanco crowded up to her side to peep into the mirror. She let him jingle the little bells.

"The strange man is good, I think," Chanco said, looking wise for his four years. "I shall always be kind to him, as you tell me."

"The day we were there," Raw-hunt went on, when the excitement over the presents had died down, "there came another of those great canoes with white wings. They called it a ship."

"Is it there still?" asked Chanco. "I want to go and see it."

A sudden thought struck Pocahontas. "I think they will want more corn now. Suppose we all go and take some to them."

She said this to some of the other girls.

The young women took up the saying too. "Let us all go," they cried. Everyone was eager to see the strange village and the big canoe.

"You must be careful," said the older women. "Some of them are still our enemies. We did not adopt them all."

"The captain promised me," said Pocahontas. "He said that whenever I came, I should call out for him and remind him that he is my pale-faced father. No one would ever harm me, he said."

"Ah!" said Aunt Teemo. "Playful Girl is not at all afraid."

"Why, I really adopted the captain first," said Pocahontas.

The older women laughed a little, but did not make any more objection.

In a day or two Pocahontas and a group of girls and young women started out, all carrying baskets of corn. They went through the cold winter woods toward the village of which they had heard so much.

The warriors said the palefaces had named their village Jamestown. This was in honor of their king, who lived in a land far away beyond the salt water. The palefaces called themselves Englishmen.

The young women came slowly up to where the pale-faced men were living. Down at the water's edge they could see the great ship of which Raw-hunt had told them.

They did not dare go near either the ship or the village. Young trees had been cut off and thrust into the ground to make a fence all around the village. They could not see inside.

"I am sure there are shooting sticks pointed out at us," said one of the girls.

"Look! The sticks shine in the sunlight!" cried Fisher Girl.

They all shivered in fright. They could almost feel the deadly balls flying right out of the guns toward them.

"Don't be afraid," said Pocahontas encouragingly. "They know we are friends."

Still they shrank back from the village and its shooting sticks.

Pocahontas went forward alone, until she stood quite near the fence. "Captain Smith! Captain Smith!" she called in as loud a voice as she could. "This is your friend, Playful Girl! Nonpareil, you called me!"

After a moment the gate was pushed open. A man with a shooting stick looked out. He saw the child standing all alone. He stood there, saying nothing.

"All right!" called a voice from behind him.

Captain Smith came outside the gate and

waved his hand, first to Playful Girl and then to the others. "Come on in!" he cried.

Playful Girl rushed up to him. "We brought you some corn, my father," she called out.

He looked at the generously filled baskets, as the others came up behind her. He smiled at the group of girls and young women.

"This will make all Jamestown happy," he said. "Such a kind and generous child you are, Playful Girl. Truly, I made no mistake when I named you Nonpareil!"

Visits to
Jamestown

A FEW days later there was a great fire in the village. The Indians thought that Jamestown was nearly destroyed. Many houses had been burned to the ground, and only the walls of others were standing. The storehouse and new church were completely destroyed.

Powhatan's warriors were glad to hear this. They did not like the strange Englishmen. The Indians pretended to be friendly, but all the time they were waiting for a good chance to fight the new enemy.

"This would be a good time to attack them," said the warriors to one another. "If we should come near and fall upon them suddenly, we might be rid of them all."

Down the river to the palefaces' town soon went a long line of warriors. Each brought a turkey or some other food. They offered to trade the food for swords and shooting sticks. They thought the newcomers would be so hungry they would be glad to trade.

They found they were mistaken, however. The English knew that without their guns and swords they would not be safe. They knew they could not trust the Indians.

Away the warriors traveled with their game, followed by hungry looks as they went.

The warriors had done what they wished to do, though. Their sharp eyes had seen what had been burned and where they could attack most easily. They made up their minds to come back in the night.

That night, to their surprise, they found the

pale-faced men waiting. There was a short sharp
fight. The shooting sticks roared out, and the
dark warriors hurried back into the forest. Three
were missing. The pale-faced men had captured
them. The Indians sent a few warriors back to
ask the sentry for the prisoners.

"Tell your Head Chief that first he must send
us food," they were told by the sentry.

Captain Smith came out beside the sentry.
"Tell your chief that if he wishes me to believe
that he wants peace and not war, it will be better
for his daughter to come."

Again Playful Girl brought gifts, and was
received kindly by the captain.

The warriors wished to claim the captives, but
Captain Smith told them, "I will give them to no
one but Pocahontas herself."

To Pocahontas the captain said, "Take these
men to your father, and say to him that we return
these captives, not because he is a chief or be-

cause he has many warriors. We are sending them back because he has a daughter in whose friendship we trust."

Pocahontas felt proud as the three captives walked behind her on the way home.

During the rest of the cold weather and in the spring when the woods were green again, she and her friends came often, bringing food for the people of Jamestown.

Sometimes she would linger to play on the white sand along the river. Chanco might be with her, and other young friends. They would have a game of leapfrog or tag before they turned back on their long walk home.

Now Captain Newport, who had sailed the big ship over the salt water, brought many more men to live with the palefaces at Jamestown. With them was one boy a year or two older than Pocahontas herself.

"We are going to take him out to your father's

village," Captain Smith told her. "Then you can teach him to talk in your own language."

Pocahontas nodded. "He will then teach me more of your way of talking."

"You are doing very well already, Pocahontas," said her pale-faced father. "You are the first person of all your race to learn to speak the English language. Someday your people will be proud of you. You have two fine things—a quick mind and a kind, loving heart."

Playful Girl felt her heart swell with pride. Indeed she would do all she could to help this boy—Thomas Savage—to learn her language.

GOLD?

"Captain Smith says that Captain Newport is a great chief," said Aunt Teemo, "but I think he is not nearly so clever as Captain Smith himself."

"You are right," said Raw-hunt. "When the

two came up here to our village, Captain Newport spread out everything he had to give. Then our Head Chief gave him only two or three small baskets of corn for them. It was silly for the captain to give so much and get so little."

"All the women were laughing," said Aunt Teemo. "We saw how cleverly Powhatan fooled him. It was hard for us not to laugh out loud."

"Captain Smith was not fooled," Raw-hunt went on. "He told how precious those blue beads of his were, so he got all the corn he could take in exchange. Perhaps it was the women who were fooled that time."

"Perhaps not so much as you think," replied Aunt Teemo. Then she closed her lips tight and said nothing more.

Pocahontas thought she knew what Aunt Teemo meant. Many of the aunts were friendly to the yellow-haired captain. When the girls were making ready to go down to Jamestown one of the older women always came out at the last moment to add something more.

Now that Thomas Savage was in their village, everyone was more curious than ever. They crowded around him whenever he came near. Most of the time he was with Pocahontas. She was busily teaching him her own language.

Thomas Savage and she were good friends. She showed him where all the new green things were coming in the woods. Sometimes they helped Raw-hunt to scare away the crows, and they found it great fun.

Down at Jamestown the men were beginning to dig up the ground and plant the seed as the Indian women did.

"They will have food of their own when it is time for the leaves to fall," said Playful Girl.

The men from the ship were not doing anything so useful as this, though. They had found a small hill where the dirt was bright-colored, like the circle Pocahontas wore on her chain. Every day they dug up quantities of this dirt and carried it to the ship.

"Whatever are they going to do with that dirt?" Pocahontas asked Thomas.

"They say it will be gold, like that ring of yours," the boy told her.

"Gold," Pocahontas repeated. "Ring." She rubbed her fingers over the yellow circlet. "This is hard, though, and that is just dust."

"They think they can make it hard," Thomas said, "and then they will make money of it."

"Money?" This was another new word.

Thomas Savage found it hard to explain. "They trade it for things they want to eat or to wear—oh, anything."

"Why will people give them useful things for just something hard and yellow?"

"Oh, they trade it again for something else."

"Oh, I see!" said Pocahontas.

"Is this money?" she asked, showing him the ring on her chain.

"No-o," he said. "That is to wear, not to trade."

"It's too big for my finger," she told him. Even for her largest finger it was still too loose.

"It's for grown-up ladies," Thomas told her. "They call it a wedding ring."

"Wedding?" This too was a new word. She pronounced it carefully.

"I have seen a wedding," he went on. "It was in a church."

"Church? Oh, I know what that is—down at the palefaces' village," said Playful Girl.

"Well, back in England a church is a big building," Thomas told her, "but they say and do the same things here. When it is a wedding, a man and a woman stand up together and listen to what the book says. The man puts a ring on the woman's finger, and they are married."

"I should like to see that," said Pocahontas.

114

Before the hot summer came Captain Newport sailed away. The bottom of his ship was full of the yellow dirt.

"Ho, ho!" cried the Indians. "How foolish those men are to work so hard just for some earth

that isn't even good enough to raise corn and pumpkins!"

Captain Smith went sailing too, this summer, but not so far as Captain Newport and his men. Instead, he went up into the big bay called the Chesapeake.

All around were different tribes of Indians. Wherever he went Captain Smith tried to make friends with the people and learn from them about the country beyond their villages.

The Indians found that he was looking for a way to the west. All the explorers hoped to travel across America and over to China and India, where they had heard of great treasures.

All summer Captain Smith went in and out of the waters of Chesapeake Bay, but he did not find the way to China.

Pocahontas was glad when her white father came back to Jamestown. She had not enjoyed going down there when he was away.

Soon there came other news. Captain Newport with his big ship had come back again from across the far waters.

"The gold dust was not good," Raw-hunt told Pocahontas. "They make many things hard with fire, so they say, but this they could not turn to stone. Ho, ho! It was all thrown away.

"Captain Newport told the King of England how great a man our Head Chief is, so in the ship have come many presents for him from the King. The palefaces want him to come down to Jamestown to get them."

"H-m-m!" said Aunt Teemo. "Let them come up here. He will not go down to them."

In a few days Captain Smith and four men came up the river in a small boat to invite the Head Chief to visit Jamestown.

Powhatan and his hunters had gone off into the forest. "They will be back another day," Raw-hunt told the palefaces.

They settled down beside a campfire to wait. "Aren't you afraid?" said one of them to Smith.

The captain shook his head. "Powhatan is often cruel," he said, "but I count on the friendship of his favorite daughter, Pocahontas. She once saved my life."

"She is a princess?" asked one of those who had just come over from England with Captain Newport.

"These people know nothing about princesses," said Smith.

"Her father is their king, isn't he? Our king has sent a crown for him."

"He is only the sort of king these wild people in the woods have," said Captain Smith. "They obey no one as our English people obey King James. Though they call one man Head Chief and his brother War Chief, they follow them only when they choose. They obey only what they consider the custom of their people."

"Why, they don't know what it means to be a king!" said the newcomer.

"Well, we shall tell them," said one of the other men.

Then, as they sat by the fire in the darkness, they heard a great shout and uproar coming from the woods around them. They began to fear the Indians were preparing to kill them. Still, those who were near them—the women and older men—did not look fierce. They only seemed to be waiting for something to happen. The Englishmen drew their swords.

Then Pocahontas rushed forward to Captain Smith. "There is no danger," she told him. "Aren't you my English father? See, you may run that sword through me if we mean to do you any wrong."

"Yes! Yes!" shouted the others. "We're only waiting for the Indian girls to dance. They won't harm you."

"It's all right," said Captain Smith quietly. "I've never known this girl to do anything that was not friendly."

The men took their places again by the fire. Pocahontas went back among the trees.

Soon she came out at the head of a troop of thirty girls. She did not look like the girl who came to Jamestown with baskets of corn. Instead, she carried a bow and arrows. To her braided hair was fastened a pair of deer horns. An otter skin hung at her waist and another was draped over her shoulder.

All the girls were dressed like this. They were painted with red or black paint. As they danced about, their shadows made strange patterns in the flickering firelight.

They kept up a loud chanting. Graceful and swift they were, like wild creatures of the forest. The Englishmen watched in wonder.

For an hour or more the girls danced and sang.

120

At the end all waved torches of burning pine which reflected strangely on their painted faces and bodies.

"A strange sight, indeed," said the Englishmen, "and a beautiful one."

"It is the custom of our people," said Pocahontas. "Before long we shall do this for our own villages. Do not your girls at home dance in this way?"

Captain Smith smiled. "Well, I have seen many dances, but nothing like this one."

"I wish I could see the girls in your country dance," said Playful Girl.

Captain Smith
Is Gone

THE leaves were turning bright when Captain Newport brought the copper crown to place on the head of Powhatan. He did not make the Head Chief more friendly by doing this. Instead, Powhatan felt that the white men must be really afraid of him.

The weather turned cold. Then some news came that made Playful Girl decide she would go down to the English village once more.

Thomas Savage had been down there, and when he came back he said, "Pocahontas, do you remember what I told you about the ring you used to wear?"

Pocahontas nodded. "You told me it was for a wedding."

"Well, there is to be a wedding at Jamestown. Ann, the girl who came on Captain Newport's ship, is to be married. Now, if you were in the town, you could see a wedding."

"Yes, I could," she said. She did not tell him, but she made up her mind to go.

She would have to go off in secret. Her father no longer liked to have her visit the English village. "Let them go hungry," he would say, with a fierce frown on his wrinkled forehead.

Her old friend Fisher Girl wanted to go too. They decided to leave before the sun was up. No one would see them go.

When they came down to the river, they found someone curled up in a canoe, waiting for them. It was Chanco. He wanted to go along.

"Oh, Chanco," said Fisher Girl, "you can never go as fast as we want to travel!"

Chanco puckered up his face as if he were going to cry.

"I want to go," he said over and over.

"Let's take him along," said Pocahontas.

"Bother!" said Fisher Girl. "I just know we'll have to carry him all the way."

They started off on their long journey. Chanco trotted right beside them.

The sun was getting high when they heard a voice call them. They were startled at first, but it was a familiar voice.

"I know who it is—it's my brother, Brave Son," said Playful Girl.

Sure enough, he was soon beside them. "Now what are you three doing?" he asked them, pretending to be stern and surprised.

He looked down quite severely at Chanco. Chanco knew him well, and only smiled back.

"We want to go to Jamestown, Brave Son," said Fisher Girl.

"To see the wedding," Playful Girl added.

"So that's it?" replied her brother. "Well, maybe that is where I am going too. I did not tell my father about it either."

The girls looked down. Then he laughed and they could not help laughing a little, too. They all went on together.

"Someday," the young man said, "we shall have horses such as Captain Newport brought for the men at Jamestown."

"When you have one, may I ride on it sometimes?" said Chanco.

"Perhaps," said Nantaqua. "Just now it will be better for you to use me as your horse for a little while."

He knelt down and the boy threw his arms around the young man's neck. "Now, hold on tight and you shall have a good ride."

This was fun for little Chanco and it helped them all to get on faster.

They were rather tired when they reached Jamestown, but they were happy to be in time for the wedding. All the people were crowding into the little church.

At one end stood the preacher in his long black gown. He had a book in his hand. Facing him were Ann Burras and John Layden.

"See!" Fisher Girl whispered. "The young woman has a mantle over her face!"

"It is called a veil," Playful Girl whispered back. "Thomas told me about it. Isn't it pretty?"

Then everyone in the church was very quiet while the preacher read from his book.

Pocahontas felt her heart leap up when John Layden took a little gold ring and placed it on Ann's finger. She thought of her yellow ring. She had lost it that night when the girls had danced. She had often looked for it since then, but had never found it.

Soon the ceremony was over, and everyone

126

was crowding around Ann. They now called her "Mistress Layden."

"I see that is another way of getting a new name," said Pocahontas to herself. "I still have more names than she has, though."

"We shall have to hurry back as fast as we can go," said Nantaqua, when the guests were beginning to leave. "Father will be very angry when he hears that you have been here."

"Oh, but I want to come again!" said Playful Girl. "I can see that they need more corn and good things to eat."

"Listen, Pocahontas," her brother began. He did not usually speak to her in a serious tone of voice. Now his words were almost cross. "Our father does not wish any of us to let the palefaces have even a single grain of corn. He threatens to kill anyone who helps them.

"I know he will be very angry if he should find out that you and Fisher Girl have been here for the wedding. You girls must keep entirely out of his sight for a day or two."

Pocahontas looked very sober now.

"If you come down again, I know he will punish you severely indeed," added Nantaqua.

128

Sadly Pocahontas nodded her head and told Nantaqua she would do as he said.

Many times, as the cold winter went on, she thought of the people at Jamestown. She wondered if Ann, now Mistress Layden, were hungry. Most of all she wondered about Captain Smith. Did he hope that the girl whom he called Nonpareil would come again with baskets of food for his people?

POWHATAN'S PLANS

It was still cold when one day Aunt Teemo called to Pocahontas and said, "Child, your father wishes to see you."

Pocahontas went to her father. When she stood before him he was frowning.

"Can you go through the woods to the village of the pale-faced men?" he asked her.

"Why, yes, Father," she answered. She had

been there many times before. Why should he ask her such a question?

"I want you to go for me and take a message to Captain Smith."

"Yes, Father," she answered again.

"Tell him I know of his need for food. Tell him that he must send us some men to build me a house. Tell him to sail his boat up the river and bring me swords and guns. I will see that he has corn in return."

"I will go at once," Pocahontas said.

Her father had not said a word about taking any food to the hungry Englishmen. She was to go empty-handed. She was afraid her father meant to do harm to Captain Smith if he came.

When she reached the village she looked down shyly and repeated her father's message to Captain Smith. He watched her steadily but asked no questions. He too felt that her father meant to do them harm.

"The two men who will build a house for your father," he told her, "will go across the land with you. I shall start at once with the boat, but it will take a little longer."

As it happened, many cold winter days passed before the people of Powhatan's village saw the ship coming up the icy river. The Englishmen had had to stop at an Indian village on the way because of the ice.

"Beware of old Powhatan," these people told Smith, when he came to trade with them. "Already he is gathering his warriors together to attack and kill you."

Captain Smith knew that they were telling him the truth. Yet he had no choice but to go on.

He must act as if Powhatan were friendly and do his best to buy the corn that would keep the hungry English alive.

He would have to be on guard every moment. It took a brave and a wise man to deal with these strange Indians. They were kind at one time and cruel only a minute later.

It was weeks before the ship reached a place opposite Powhatan's village. Even then it was impossible to bring it all the way to the shore.

The old Head Chief and his warriors had been making their plans. The fighting men were all hidden near by, ready to attack the English.

"My father means to harm these people," said Pocahontas to Aunt Teemo. "I can see he is getting ready to fight them."

Aunt Teemo shook her head sadly.

"Can't we do anything to help?" Pocahontas asked Raw-hunt.

"I am afraid, child," he answered, "that there is nothing we can do."

When Pocahontas went to Nantaqua, her brother, he too had no answer for her. "If you try to do anything," he told his sister, "Father will punish you."

132

He said this so seriously that it made her shiver to think about it.

Pocahontas talked to Chanco about it.

"Chanco," she said thoughtfully, "those people have all been very kind to me. They treat me as if I were what they call a princess. Captain Smith is like a father. My own father might tell the men with clubs to hit me, but I am sure Captain Smith never would do such a thing.

"I would never want to hurt any of them. I don't like all this fighting and hurting, anyway. I want you to promise me that you will always be friendly to Captain Smith's people."

Chanco was still very young, but he could understand what Pocahontas meant. "I promise," he told her. He laid his hand over his heart, to show her that he really meant it.

"Now don't tell anybody what I have said," she went on, "but come and tell me what you see and hear as you go around the village."

At last the boat with Captain Smith came up the icy river. The weather was bitterly cold.

None of Powhatan's people came out to greet the Englishmen. When the old Head Chief saw Captain Smith, he pretended he had never sent for him.

"I have no corn for you," he said, "unless you give me guns and swords."

Then he disappeared, and soon a group of angry warriors pressed around the captain. They threatened him with their spears.

Smith drew his sword and struck the men around him so fiercely that they were glad to retreat and let him make his way back to the shore, where the boat was anchored.

"The boat cannot go until the tide turns," he said. "We must stay here until then."

"They intend to make war on us," said one of the men to him.

134

"You are right," said Captain Smith. "The women and children are all out of sight, and all of the men are painted as though they were going into battle."

There was an empty hut near the edge of the water. Here Smith and his companions built a fire to keep themselves warm until the boat could leave when the tide turned.

They kept their weapons close beside them as they sat by the fire. It was dark now. Their only light was from the burning logs.

Suddenly Captain Smith caught sight of a slender figure coming through the trees.

"Nonpareil!" he said, as the Indian girl drew near to the hut.

Pocahontas was out of breath from running. She was trembling with fear for her friends.

"My father means harm to you," she said to Captain Smith. "You must go away at once. He plans to kill you all."

"Then he will not give us the corn he has promised?" asked one of the Englishmen.

"No, not a grain of corn," said Pocahontas. "He will pretend to be friendly, but you must put no trust in what he says. When you are not expecting them, his warriors will fall upon you and destroy you all.

"'Now I must go. I must hurry back to the women before anyone notices I have been gone."

"You faithful girl!" said Captain Smith. "You are a true friend. We shall leave as soon as the tide turns and we can go up the river.

"First let us give you some of the things you love to have."

"No! No!" cried Pocahontas. Tears came to her eyes and rolled slowly down her brown cheeks. "Indeed I would not dare to take anything. If my father thought I had come to warn you, he would tell his warriors to kill me, just as they once tried to dash out your brains."

She vanished into the woods. When the tide turned, the ship sailed away, to seek other villages where corn might be bought for the starving people of Jamestown.

SAD NEWS

Spring came and then summer. It was more than two years since Chanco had stood on the rock and had had a far-off glimpse of the white-winged canoes of the English. Now more of the big canoes were coming.

Pocahontas did not go down to Jamestown as she had done before.

Powhatan grew more and more angry. "They come to take our lands away from us," he said.

"I forbid you to carry them anything," he told Pocahontas. "Let them stay hungry. Maybe they will go away sooner."

Pocahontas fretted, but she did not dare disobey her father. She hoped that someday he would have a kinder feeling and would again let her visit the English people in the village down the river.

She listened eagerly to any news that came from Jamestown. Indian men lurked in the trees about the settlement. They came back after a while to tell what they had seen and heard.

Then a sad piece of news came. The fierce old Head Chief smiled when he heard it. It made Pocahontas unhappy. Captain Smith, they learned, had been hurt.

He had gone with some other Englishmen on a trip into the bay. On the way back he had been sleeping on the deck of a boat. A bullet was accidentally shot into a bag of powder near by. There was a loud noise. A great puff of smoke burst out into the air all around. When the men could see what had happened, they found that Captain Smith was very badly injured.

"His skin was all torn off on one side," said Raw-hunt, who was telling her the story. "It is all raw and bleeding. I heard a man say that no one knew how to cure him."

Pocahontas shivered. "Could he get up and walk away?" she asked.

"Not at all," Raw-hunt told her.

"He must be dead," the Indians said.

"Maybe it is a trick to fool us," said Powhatan.

In time, however, as the autumn went on, he too began to believe that the English captain was no longer alive.

Pocahontas grieved about it. She had been proud to be the friend of the pale-faced captain. It made her heart happy when he praised her for her kindness.

"They must be right. I'm afraid he is dead," she said to herself. "I won't go any more to the English village. He will no longer be there to smile at me and tell me to come in."

Pocahontas among the Palefaces

SEVERAL years had gone by since Captain Smith had been in Jamestown. Playful Girl was almost grown-up now. She felt too old to play leapfrog any longer, or turn handsprings on the sand, or stand on her head. She wore her string of beautiful white pearls all the time.

She never went to Jamestown any more. There was no English father to greet her there. She seldom used the English words Captain Smith had taught her.

It was summertime in the year 1613. Pocahontas had gone up to the village on the Potomac River where her Aunt Jappy lived. Here she felt a bit more peaceful. Her aunt and uncle did not fight the palefaces. They even traded with a ship that came up the river, under Captain Argall. Pocahontas was glad to be away from all the talk of battles.

One morning she and Aunt Jappy walked up to the falls. Pocahontas was happy to see her old friend Arrow Maker.

"Here, young Playful Girl!" he called out to her. "Are you ready to hunt for some good stones for me to work on?"

"Of course I am, my friend," she answered. "I wonder if I shall be as good at picking them out as I used to be?"

"You'll soon learn to do it again," he told her. "Here come some men from a distant village to trade some things for arrows. Wait and see what they have to offer us."

When the trading party came up, Pocahontas glanced for only a minute at their pack of skins.

Instead, she looked very hard at a young man who was with them.

He was doing the talking for his party. He spoke in her own language. He was tall and straight and dark, a fine powerful young man. And yet there was something about him that made her think of a boy no taller than she had been four or five years before.

The young man looked around him. Then his eyes rested upon her. He too looked surprised. Suddenly his eyes lighted up. He remembered she had been his playmate.

Pocahontas remembered him at almost the very same moment.

"Playful Girl!" cried the young man and ran quickly to her side.

"Captive Boy!" Pocahontas cried out. "Where did you go when I lost you, so long ago?"

Captive Boy laughed. "I almost lost myself," he answered. "I thought I was near my home, but it was farther than I believed. It was days before I found it. I wandered around in the cold woods and nearly starved."

"You might have been frozen. It was during a cold time."

"I did not think of that when I dodged out of your sight. All I thought of was to get back to my own home."

"I went to my home, too," said Pocahontas.

"Oh, yes," he said, "I heard about that—how you saved the English captain by putting your own head between him and the men that were going to kill him."

"He is gone now," said Pocahontas. "I used to call him my pale-faced father."

"I heard about his being hurt, too. Now your father Head Chief wants us all to refuse to trade with the English at Jamestown, but our people are not fighting anyone just now.

"Often, when our people have to come up

here, I come along to help in the talk. That is because you taught me to use your language so long ago, Playful Girl."

Pocahontas laughed. "Walk," she said, and began to walk up and down, as she had done to teach him.

"Tree," he said, and pointed to a pine tree growing near by.

They laughed together, remembering how she had been his teacher.

"You are the same Playful Girl you used to be, years ago," said he, "but I am no longer a Captive Boy."

They walked back to the village. Aunt Jappy said, "Think now, Pocahontas. That fine young man would be my son today, if you had not helped him to run away."

Aunt Jappy's voice sounded cross. Pocahontas wondered if her aunt were still angry with her for what had happened long years before.

A few days after this, Captain Argall came sailing up the river. Everyone in the village turned out to see him.

He had many interesting and useful things. Best of all was a handsome copper kettle.

Aunt Jappy talked a great deal about that copper kettle. How much more useful it would be, she told the other women, than their homemade kettles. It would hold so much more. It would be so much stronger. It would never break.

The copper kettle would take a great many things in exchange if they were to get it from the English captain. Pocahontas did not know that her uncle had been planning a different kind of trading with the captain.

Old Head Chief Powhatan had captive Englishmen in his village. He had also many things which his warriors had taken away from them—hoes, axes, guns, and swords.

146

Captain Argall thought he knew a way to get these back again. He would take the chief's daughter. Then he would bargain with Powhatan to trade her for the English captives and the stolen goods.

"Bring your niece on board here," he said to the aunt and uncle, "and you shall have the copper kettle for your own."

They worked out a plan. Pocahontas knew nothing about it.

One afternoon Uncle came back from visiting the ship. He seemed in good spirits. He told Aunt about many things he had seen.

"Oh, I want to see it too!" she cried out. "Can't you take me on board the ship?"

Uncle shook his head. "Such a visit is not for a woman."

Pocahontas began to feel that she would like to see the English ship too. She looked over at Aunt Jappy and smiled.

That was what Aunt Jappy wanted. "Pocahontas has seen English ships, long summers ago," she cried. "Why can't we both go with you to see it? Pocahontas could talk to the captain in his own language."

Uncle pretended to think. He could see that Pocahontas was beginning to be interested. "Well, I must see about it," he said slowly.

He went off again to where the ship was lying. When Uncle came back, he said that Captain Argall had invited them both to see the ship. They set off at once.

Captain Argall greeted them kindly. To Pocahontas he spoke some words in his own language. She answered in the same way.

Aunt Jappy admired everything she saw. "It is wonderful!" she declared. "I am so happy you let us come."

She lingered so long over everything that the sun was low in the west. Then Captain Argall said, "There is food waiting for us in my cabin. Let us eat together."

The three followed him to a room where a table had been set with good things.

Aunt and Uncle laughed heartily at the dishes and knives and forks. Pocahontas remembered these from her visits to Jamestown.

It was a very merry meal. Pocahontas began to forget that Aunt Jappy had still seemed cross with her only a few days ago.

Captain Argall then took them to the wheel which helped to guide the boat. He let Pocahontas put her hand upon it.

"When the sails are up and the breeze is blowing," he told her, "we turn this wheel. It makes the ship turn so that the breeze can swell out the sails and move us along over the water."

Pocahontas was so interested that for some time she did not notice that Aunt and Uncle had gone away. One minute Aunt Jappy had been peering over her shoulder at the wheel. Then, strangely, she was quite out of sight.

Pocahontas was frightened when she found that she was alone with the captain.

"Where are my uncle and aunt?" she cried out in alarm.

She heard a sound of paddling. Looking out in the dusk, she saw a canoe on the water, leaving the ship. Uncle was wielding the paddle very gently. Aunt Jappy sat in the middle. There was a broad smile on her face. She was running her hands lovingly over the surface of a copper kettle on her lap. The last rays of the setting sun touched the kettle and made it shine.

"Aunt Jappy! Aunt Jappy!" called Pocahontas loudly. "Come back!"

Aunt Jappy had no eyes for her.

Pocahontas ran to the side of the ship. She was about to jump into the water.

Captain Argall put his hand gently on her

arm. "You must stay with us," he said. His voice was not unkind.

"No! No!" she protested.

"We shall treat you kindly," he said. "You must not be afraid of us. We will return you to your father when he sends back to us what he has taken away.

"Early in the morning we shall set sail for Jamestown."

The Captive
Pocahontas

From Jamestown a messenger was sent to Chief Powhatan.

"Your daughter is well and kindly treated," the Head Chief was told, "but she must stay with us until you send back your prisoners. You must also return the guns and swords that have been taken from us."

Powhatan listened silently.

"We shall send you an answer later," one of the warriors told the messenger.

The messenger went back to Jamestown with empty hands.

"Chanco," said Aunt Teemo one day, "can't

you get down to Jamestown and see how our Pocahontas is getting along? We miss her here. We hope she is well treated."

Chanco was only too glad to go. In fact, he had been planning to attempt the journey to the English village. Now, with Aunt Teemo to help him, he knew that he could go safely.

He was afraid when he came near the village. He had not been at Jamestown since the time when he and Pocahontas had gone to see the wedding. He had been very glad then to be carried a good part of the distance. He laughed as he thought of that journey. Now he felt that before long he might be as tall as Nantaqua himself.

An Englishman stood at the gate. Chanco was glad that he remembered the English words Pocahontas had taught him.

"I come as a friend," he told the sentry, very seriously. "I am alone and I carry no weapons. I come to see my friend Pocahontas."

The pale-faced man considered him for a moment. "You may come in," he said. He stood aside so that the boy might enter the gate. "She is at the home of our rector, Mr. Whitaker."

Down the straight row of houses went Chanco. Pocahontas saw him on his way and came outside to meet him.

How glad they were to see each other!

"You cannot carry me off this rock, Chanco, as I carried you when we first saw the canoes with wings," said Pocahontas. She was half laughing and half crying. "Won't my father send back the things he has taken, and the prisoners? Or doesn't he want me to come back?"

"I think he will send some," Chanco told her, "but you know some of the prisoners are not alive any longer, and some have run away. Your father did not promise to do anything, but warriors have gone out to other villages to find them."

"Tell Aunt Teemo they are all kind to me,"

said Pocahontas. "They never speak of Captain Smith, though. I think often of the time when he was here."

"I wish he were here now," said Chanco.

"So do I," said Pocahontas. "They are all friendly, though. Mr. Whitaker teaches me more English words from the black book he reads in the church in the mornings. He explains to me what the strange words mean. I like to hear him talk. His wife teaches me the things they do in their homes, too. Tell Aunt Teemo she must not be sad about me."

It was time for Chanco to go back.

"Tell Raw-hunt I miss him, too," said Pocahontas, as the boy started away.

Three months went by before any other word came from Head Chief Powhatan. Then, one day, some warriors brought seven of the English prisoners and a few old muskets and swords.

"Where are the other prisoners?" asked Gov-

ernor Thomas Dale. He was head of the Jamestown settlement.

The warriors only shook their heads. This was
all they had to give.

Raw-hunt was with them. "What does my
father say?" Pocahontas asked him.

"He says very little," Raw-hunt told her. "He
is still angry with the pale-faced men. He wishes
to drive them out of the country."

When the next spring came Governor Dale
grew tired of waiting for the wily Chief Powhatan to answer him.

"We shall take the ships we have here," he
said to Pocahontas, "and you with us. We shall
sail up to your father's village and I myself shall
talk with him."

When the English ships came up the river to
the bank near which the village stood, they found
that Powhatan was not there. He was away with
his warriors. Governor Dale and his ships sailed

back to Jamestown, taking Pocahontas with them. She was very unhappy.

"Does my father care more for guns and axes than he does for me?" she cried.

TWO CEREMONIES

Pocahontas was back again in the English village. Sometimes Raw-hunt, in his swift journeys from one town to another, would find time to stop in Jamestown to see her and tell her about her aunts and other relatives.

"There is a young man here," Pocahontas told him, "who is planting large fields of tobacco. He says that he can dry it and tie it up in bundles. The ships will take it back to England.

"Isn't it strange," she went on, "that in that far country over the ocean, men never saw tobacco and never knew anything about it?

"Corn, too. They did not know what that

was either. It would seem strange to have no corn to eat."

"Indeed, we would not like to do without it." Raw-hunt agreed.

"Tell my aunts I miss them all and would love to see them," said Pocahontas. "Everyone is good to me here, though—especially the young man who is raising tobacco. His name is John—John Rolfe.

"If I can help to make my father treat these English people better, I want to do it."

Pocahontas had still more to say.

"Raw-hunt, tell my people I go to English church twice every Sunday. They are going to make me a member of it, like themselves. I wish you could all come and see what it is like.

"Captain Smith used to say that I was the first of our people to learn to talk in his language. Now they tell me I am the first one to be taken into their church."

Some of the Indians were there when Pocahontas knelt before the altar of the Jamestown church. She was dressed all in white, like an English girl. When the water was sprinkled on her head, she heard the voice of the minister saying, "I baptize thee Rebecca."

"So now I have still another name," she told Chanco, who had watched the ceremony in amazement. "It will not be long, either, before I shall have still another. Tell my aunts that the young man of whom I spoke to Raw-hunt is going to be my husband."

"Do you mean John Rolfe?" Chanco asked.

"Yes. Chanco, do you remember how we long ago watched the first wedding they had here in Jamestown? Do you also remember the little gold ring Nantaqua brought me that was lost? Now I am going to have another ring, and when John Rolfe puts it on my finger they will call me Mistress Rolfe.

160

"Chanco, the people here have sent messengers to my father to ask his permission for the marriage to take place. I do so hope this is going to make us all friends, as we were when Captain Smith was here."

Powhatan gave his consent to his daughter's marriage to John Rolfe. He promised to remain friendly. However, he would not come to Jamestown to see the wedding in April, 1614.

Uncle Fierce War Chief was there, and her brother Nantaqua. Raw-hunt and Chanco looked on in wonder while the minister read from a black book. Then John Rolfe put a small gold ring on Pocahontas' finger. The minister said, "I now pronounce you man and wife."

Then all the people crowded up to welcome her, calling her Mistress Rolfe.

"How kind they all are," she later said to Chanco. "Remember, my friend—you must always be kind to them."

To Raw-hunt she said, "It will make me very happy if my father will remain at peace with these English. They are my people now."

"You have another name now, Mistress Rebecca Rolfe," said her new husband to her, with a fond smile.

"A very fine name," she answered proudly, smiling up at him.

In her heart she thought of the name another Englishman had given her, and to herself she said, "I wish Captain Smith might have seen our wedding. I would have liked to hear him call me Nonpareil."

Tomocomo's Story

"I wish I could go across the big water," said Chanco. He was growing to be a tall boy.

In 1616, Governor Dale of Jamestown returned to England for a visit. He took a party of Indians with him.

John Rolfe went, too, and with him his wife and their baby. They called the baby Thomas, in honor of Governor Dale.

"The people of England will never think that Pocahontas is really an Indian," said the Governor. "Though her hair is black and her cheeks are brown, she seems in every way like an English wife and mother. The people in England will call her the Lady Rebecca, or perhaps Princess Pocahontas.

"If they are to see real Indians, we must have with us some people from Powhatan's village," the Governor decided.

Powhatan gave his consent. He hadn't fought the English since his daughter had married John Rolfe. One of the sisters of Pocahontas, Matachanna, was going with her husband, Tomocomo. Other young Indian men and women were going. Chanco was not one of those chosen to make the trip, however.

"Keep your eyes open in this country on the other side of the big water," said Powhatan to Tomocomo. "Mark down on a string how many people there are, tie a knot for each one, and bring it back to me. Also, see if there are any trees or cornfields there."

Tomocomo tried to do this in England. Very soon, though, he saw that even if he had more string, he could not tie knots fast enough to count all the people in England. In disgust he soon threw the string away.

Traveling by coach from Plymouth to London, Tomocomo discovered that England indeed had many trees and grain fields.

All of the Indians were glad to come back to their own land, Virginia. Pocahontas and her little son Thomas did not return to their homeland with the others.

"We were in a village so large that we could not count the houses," Tomocomo told his people back home. "Even the streets were too many for us to count."

Cries of "Oh!" and "Ah!" arose. Could it be true that Tomocomo had seen those large buildings, those great fleets of ships, those immense crowds of people? Some of the villagers began to look very doubtfully at Tomocomo. Chanco listened to every word.

"Everywhere we went, people followed us and stared at us," the returned traveler went on. "We were invited to many houses where they asked us all sorts of questions. I was taken to meet their great King James. Pocahontas and I saw the King and Queen and many others at a Christmas mask at the court.

"Pocahontas wore clothes like the English people's. She was presented at their court as the daughter of the Indian king."

"Did Pocahontas like those people as well as those at Jamestown?" Chanco asked.

"She did not like being stared at. She did not like the crowds that followed her. Later on, though, there were many people who treated her so kindly that she enjoyed being with them.

"It was an odd thing. At first people said that the King was angry with John Rolfe for marrying our sister. The King said a commoner should not have married a princess.

"Do you remember that time long ago when Captain Smith and Captain Newport tried to make our Head Chief kneel down so they could put a round band of copper on his head?"

All his hearers nodded their heads. Some of them laughed. They remembered how hard it had been for the two Englishmen to make Powhatan bend over even a little.

Tomocomo went on. "Well, those people seemed to think that putting that thing on his head made him a king like theirs. Only their King is not a fine strong man like Powhatan. What does Powhatan care for their funny word 'king'? He is our Head Chief. That is honor enough for any man.

"The English people spoke of the Princess Pocahontas. Sometimes they called her Lady Rebecca. That was the name they gave her in the church."

"Did she like to be called princess?"

"I do not believe she did," answered Tomo-como. "She said once that, of all the different names she had, the one she liked best was the one she had been given by Captain John Smith when he was here."

"I know what that was," Chanco exclaimed eagerly. "He called her Nonpareil. He said it meant there were no other girls like her. She said that many girls and women might be called princess, but Nonpareil meant something still better than that—'nothing equal.'"

A sound of agreement went around the group. They too remembered what the blond young captain had named the girl who had put her dark head between him and the clubs of her father's warriors.

Captain Smith
Is Alive

"Now listen carefully," Tomocomo went on. "I have the most surprising thing yet to tell."

The men and women gathered closer. Chanco was closest of all. He did not wish to miss a single word.

"Someone wrote a letter to the Queen of England. The letter told what a fine girl Pocahontas is and how she had done so much to help the people of Jamestown. It told how she brought them food and tried to keep her father friendly to them all.

"Who do you suppose wrote that letter? It was Captain John Smith himself!"

A cry of astonishment went around the circle.

"I thought he was dead!" exclaimed Chanco.

"So we all thought," Tomocomo told them. "He was very badly burned when the shot set the powder bag afire. We all knew how he was carried to the ship that was leaving for England. He couldn't speak at all then. We supposed he died and was buried in the water.

"Instead of that, he was taken back to England. After a long time the doctors there were able to cure his burns and he could walk again."

"Why didn't he come back to Jamestown?" asked Aunt Teemo.

"I don't know why. Instead, he began making trips farther north—north of where the Mohawks live. Captain Smith himself told me this."

"So you saw him?"

"Oh, yes. One afternoon he came to see Pocahontas and her English husband. My wife and I were with them. He spoke to her husband with dignity and called him Master Rolfe. When he turned to Pocahontas, he bent one knee nearly down to the floor. 'Welcome to our land, Lady Rebecca' was what he said.

"Pocahontas did not like this. She drew her hand away and turned to the window. Here she sat for a long, long time. She looked out of the window. She did not say a word, either to Captain Smith or to the rest of us."

"Why wouldn't she talk to him?"

"Captain Smith did not know why. Even her husband seemed surprised."

"Oh, oh!" said one of the aunts softly.

"Captain Smith talked with John Rolfe and played a little while with the baby Thomas. Thomas had grown to be a fine boy while we were in the far country. He and the captain grew quite friendly. Still Pocahontas would not talk to the captain."

"What did the captain do then?"

"He turned toward Pocahontas as she sat at the window. 'Did I make a mistake,' he asked her, 'when I wrote to the Queen of England and told her that this Indian princess can talk in the English language? I was proud to tell her that."

"She *can* talk in the language of the English!" said the aunt who had spoken before.

"Then," said Tomocomo, "Pocahontas at last began to speak. She felt that he had treated her as if she were a stranger. 'I was told that you were dead, and I knew no better until now. Why do you call me by such names as princess and Lady Rebecca? The name you yourself gave me is what I like most to hear.'

"The captain explained that he had done this to show her how much the people of his land thought of her.

"She shook her head at this. Then she asked him if he had forgotten the name by which he used to call her in her own land.

" 'No, you are still the Nonpareil among girls,' he told her.

"The frown began to disappear from her forehead then.

" 'Did you not come to my father's country and make everyone afraid?' she reminded him. 'But I—I was not afraid! Now, are you afraid that I'll call you father in your own country, as I did when I used to come to Jamestown?

" 'I tell you that I will call you father and you shall call me child—and I shall be forever and forever your countryman.' "

Then Tomocomo added, "I think she was happier in that moment than in the weeks afterward, when she talked with the English King and Queen, and great people of power and possessions gave balls and dinners for her. Everyone praised her and admired her. I think she grew very tired of all the excitement."

Chanco
Remembers

WHILE Powhatan lived he kept his promise of friendship to the people of Jamestown. No fierce Indian warriors were sent with war whoops and flaming torches to burn homes and scalp men, women, and children. More people came over the salt water. They started farms, called plantations, and scattered over the countryside near Jamestown.

Chanco was a young man now, but he did not go on the warpath. He had never forgotten the things Pocahontas had said. Often, when he was very young indeed, she had said to him in her quiet way, "Chanco, always be friendly to

176

the pale-faced people. They are kind to us and we should be kind to them."

Now Chanco was living on the plantation of one of those pale-faced men. Here he helped to raise tobacco and harvest it.

Chanco liked his work and he liked the owner of the plantation very much. Steadily he learned more and more of the language and customs of the English people.

After Chief Powhatan was gone, the Indians chose a new Head Chief. He was a sickly man, a cripple who had never been a warrior. He too kept peace and friendship with the people from over the water. They were never molested and their farms and houses were unharmed while he was alive.

But he was old and ill. Before long he too was being mourned by the Indians. The new head chief was Opekankano, Fierce War Chief. He was Pocahontas' cruel and crafty old uncle.

He loved to brag about the many men he had killed in battle.

Fierce War Chief sent a messenger to Jamestown, with gifts and a promise to be friendly with the English people there.

"Peace between us is so firm," his messenger said to the people of Jamestown, "that the skies themselves will fall down before the chain of friendship shall be broken."

The English people were happy to hear this, and they trusted him.

The wily old Fierce War Chief was only trying to keep them believing in him until he could give them a crushing blow. For many years he had waited for the time when he could get rid of all these strange people from across the water. He hoped to kill many and drive the rest away in fright.

One night about a week after the Indian messenger had delivered his promise of peace,

Chanco was lying on his bed of skins in the tobacco barn.

He heard the lap of water. This plantation was north of the river. In the daytime they could see smoke rising from the chimneys of Jamestown. To go to the village they had to take a canoe and paddle across the stream.

Chanco heard frogs croaking in the distance. A bobwhite gave its piercing call. Through the open door of his shed Chanco could see the first stars of the evening beginning to twinkle out of the dark blue of the sky. There would be no moonlight tonight, though.

Then he heard something—a light footstep. It was dark, but he could recognize his elder brother standing in the doorway.

"I have come to spend the night with you," said his brother.

This happened often. It did not seem at all strange to Chanco to share some of his skin robes with a visitor for the night. However, as they talked about the village and the people there, Chanco began to feel that his brother had something more than a visit on his mind.

Finally his brother said, "Well, Chanco, there is something I have to tell you. Fierce War Chief has decided it is time for all of us to get together and be rid of these people who have come to our land. We don't want them here any longer."

"The messenger from Fierce War Chief said the chain of friendship would never be broken," said Chanco.

"That was just to keep the English from suspecting what we are planning to do," said his brother. "Now we are all ready. One by one the warriors are coming in to visit, as I have come to stay with you. In the morning they will ask for breakfast. They will seem happy and friendly with all the palefaces.

"Then we shall hear the war whoops of Fierce War Chief and his men. It will be the signal for us. We are to rise up and kill everyone, on the plantations and in the village. Not even one paleface must be left alive.

"After we have finished killing all the people here, we are to go to Jamestown and destroy everyone there."

Chanco shivered, though the night was not cool. He thought with horror of seeing a tomahawk in the head of the kindly Englishman he worked for.

"He has always been like a father to me," the young Indian thought.

To his brother he merely said "Yes" or "I see." He knew that nothing would turn his brother from his purpose.

"I shall wait until he is asleep and then get away," Chanco said to himself.

Chanco lay there thinking of the man who

had treated him like a son. He thought of the mother of the household, who had been kind to him. He thought of their little boy, who liked to tag around after him everywhere. "Just the way I used to follow Playful Girl," he said to himself.

Then Chanco himself fell asleep and had a dream. He remembered Pocahontas so clearly that he almost felt she was standing by his side. It was not Mistress John Rolfe that he saw, but the Playful Girl he had known long before, when he was a small child.

"Chanco," she seemed to whisper to him in his vivid dream, "remember you are always to be kind to the English people."

Just as he had said to her long ago, Chanco promised, "I will always be kind to them, Playful Girl."

Now he was awake again, and no Playful Girl stood beside him. His brother was fast asleep

182

and did not stir as Chanco slipped out from under his coverings. Chanco carefully and silently moved toward the door.

Then he was hurrying, quiet as a cat, through the barnyard and up to the door of the farm-house. He knocked very softly.

"Who is it?" said a voice from within.

"Chanco," he answered. "There will be trouble. I come to tell you."

Soon his story was told.

"We must all go at once to Jamestown to warn them," said the farmer. "No doubt the Indians will burn everything here, but if we can reach the village in time, the people there may be able to defend it and save at least part of their homes.

"You must come with us, Chanco. It would not be safe for you to stay here when they find that you have warned us."

Off down the river they went and carried the warning. The people of Jamestown made ready to protect themselves.

When the Indians came, they found men with guns guarding the town. When the war whoop sounded, all the English were ready to fight, and the Indians fled into the dark forest.

Although there was no surprise for the people of Jamestown, many whole families on the further plantations were killed and many houses were burned to the ground.

At Jamestown everybody praised Chanco warmly and told him he had saved their homes and their lives. He always felt in his heart that he had only kept his word to Playful Girl, who had told him he must always be kind to the English people.

Pocahontas, John, and Thomas

More than three hundred years have passed. Instead of a few settlers on the Atlantic Coast, there is now a great nation of many millions of palefaced people whose language is English. The people of Chief Powhatan's tribe have dwindled away.

Pocahontas never came back from England. While she and her husband and baby were waiting at Gravesend for a boat for America, she was stricken with smallpox, and died.

John Rolfe left little Thomas with an uncle in England. Thomas was educated there. He had the dark coloring and black hair of his mother.

187

Otherwise, he was just another English boy. He knew no more of Indian life and customs than did his English friends.

When his school days were over, he came back to Virginia. His father was gone. Chanco had been able to save the people of Jamestown, but there had been no time to warn the further plantations. Indian warriors killed John Rolfe.

Nevertheless, his son lived on among the English-speaking people in Virginia where he was born. He did not even think of going to dwell in the village where his mother's people still lived.

He married and had one child, a daughter. Among her descendants were many people who are important in the history of Virginia. A great-grandson was the famous John Randolph of Roanoke, long a leader in Congress a hundred years or more ago.

In later years, the wife of a President of the

United States, Mrs. Woodrow Wilson, is one of the many Virginians of the present time who are proud to trace their ancestry back to the Indian girl Pocahontas.

As the years passed, the village of Jamestown disappeared. The English people learned to farm and raise their own foodstuffs, so they were not dependent on the ships from across the ocean.

Their settlement was moved further inland. Because they now had a new King they renamed their town Williamsburg.

People always remembered Jamestown had been the first settlement of English-speaking colonists in Virginia. After three hundred years, a great Jamestown Exposition was planned to remind everyone of those long-ago days.

From all over America people came to see the place where Jamestown had stood. All that was left of its buildings was a part of the tower of the

church. Here Pocahontas had knelt in baptism to receive the name of Rebecca. Here she stood with John Rolfe to be married.

Near this ruined tower a bronze statue was placed. Great crowds of people at that Exposition of 1907 stood on this green plot of land that jutted out into the water. They saw the veil being taken from the statue, as speakers told of the life of the young woman to whom it was dedicated. It seemed fitting that this statue of Pocahonas should stand there always.

The statue shows a slight, active figure, looking out over land and water as Playful Girl herself might have done on her visits to the settlement. It is a beautiful memorial to the girl whose quick action and kind heart did so much to keep the early colony alive.

Farther north, near where Aunt Jappy lived, now stands a city which is the center of government for our nation. It was named Washington in honor of our first President. Here is the great domed Capitol building where the Congress makes laws for our land.

There is a huge circular hall in the middle of the Capitol. Its walls are covered with great pictures which represent scenes from the early history of our country. Thousands of visitors stop to see these pictures.

One picture shows a brown-skinned young woman in a white robe and veil. She is kneeling before the minister of the Jamestown church. The picture is called "The Baptism of Pocahontas."

She was a playful little Indian girl in the dark woods of early Virginia. She grew to be Mistress Rolfe of a prosperous plantation. She was called "Lady Rebecca" at the court of the English King and Queen. Surely there is no girl in history whose story is quite like hers.

Captain John Smith spoke wisely when he said that she was the girl without an equal.

More About This Book

WHEN POCAHONTAS LIVED

1595   POCAHONTAS WAS BORN IN VIRGINIA.

King James ruled in England.

Powhatan was Head Chief of the Indian tribe near the area which later was Jamestown.

About one million Indians lived in North America when European exploring began in 1600.

1607   POCAHONTAS SAVED CAPTAIN JOHN SMITH'S LIFE, IN DECEMBER.

Jamestown, Virginia, was founded by more than a hundred colonists on the left bank of the "River of Powhatan" (James River), 1607.

First cargo from America to foreign country, consisting of pitch, tar, soap, ashes, and glass, was shipped from Jamestown to England, 1608.

Captain John Smith was president of Jamestown, 1608.

1612 POCAHONTAS WAS HELD AS HOSTAGE AT JAMES-
TOWN.

New York City was founded on Manhattan
Island when the Dutch sent out two ships to
trade with the Indians on the Hudson River,
1612.

John Rolfe planted the first successful tobacco
crop in North America, 1612.

1613 POCAHONTAS WAS CONVERTED TO CHRISTIAN-
ITY AND BAPTIZED BY REVEREND ALEXANDER
WHITAKER, WHO ESTABLISHED THE FIRST
PRESBYTERIAN CONGREGATION IN VIRGINIA.

A small French settlement on the coast of
Maine was forced out by English settlers
from Jamestown, led by Captain Argall, 1613.

1614 POCAHONTAS MARRIED JOHN ROLFE.

The first large-scale fishing expedition in America, led by Captain Smith, sailed from Virginia in search of copper, gold, whales, and,
finally, fish off the coast of Maine. He caught
60,000 in one month, 1614.

The first important Dutch settlement in the
New World was the stockaded post at Al-
bany, established by Dutch fur traders, 1614.

194

1616   POCAHONTAS WENT TO ENGLAND.

A smallpox epidemic among the Indians almost destroyed tribes from the Penobscot River to Narragansett Bay, 1616.

King James proclaimed first penal colony in America, providing for the exile of the worst criminals to the colony of Virginia, 1617.

1617   POCAHONTAS DIED AT GRAVESEND, ENGLAND.

Samuel Argall was Deputy Governor of Jamestown, 1617.

The estimated population of the Virginia colony was about 1,672.

DO YOU REMEMBER?

1. What present did Nantaqua bring Pocahontas?
2. What did the Indian women use in making bread?
3. What was used to cover the frames of the Indian houses?
4. What was planted between the rows of corn?
5. What was used for a stockade around the houses?
6. What prevented Raw-hunt from being a good hunter or warrior?

7. On what did Pocahontas serve stew to her brother?

8. Who was Don Luis?

9. Of what did Aunt Teemo make a cord for Pocahontas' ring?

10. How did Pocahontas prepare rabbit skins to make clothing?

11. What did Aunt Jappy make of cattails and rushes?

12. How did the Indians make their skin garments warmer for winter?

13. How did Pocahontas dress for her dance before Captain Smith and the Englishmen?

14. How was Captain Smith injured?

15. What did Aunt Jappy trade for a copper kettle?

16. How did Pocahontas and Captive Boy meet again?

17. What names did the English people give Pocahontas?

18. What promise made to Pocahontas did Chanco keep?

19. What President's wife is a descendant of Pocahontas?

20. How was an Indian house built?

21. How did the Indians protect their crops from the birds?

22. Where is the bronze statue of Pocahontas?

IT'S FUN TO LOOK UP THESE THINGS

1. To what tribe of Indians did Pocahontas belong?

2. How did the Indians gather oysters?

3. How are pearls made?

4. When did the Spaniards come to America first?

5. To what tribe did the Susquehannoks belong?

6. Why does the compass needle point always to the north?

7. How was a cradleboard used?

8. Find out when paper was invented.

INTERESTING THINGS YOU CAN DO

1. Make a map showing Pocahontas' home village, Jamestown settlement, and Aunt Jappy's village.

2. Find pictures of sailing ships of the sixteenth and early seventeenth century, and bring them to class.

3. Make a model of an Indian house—or hut—and bring to class.

OTHER BOOKS YOU MAY ENJOY READING

Pocahontas, Ingri M. and Edgar P. Aulaire. Doubleday.

Pocahontas and Captain John Smith, Marie Abrams. Trade Edition, Random House. School Edition, Hale.

Pocahontas, Young American Princess, Mildred Criss. Dodd.

Sacagawea: Bird Girl, Flora Warren Seymour. Trade and School Editions, Bobbs-Merrill.

Story of Pocahontas, The, Shirley Graham. Grosset.

Tecumseh: Shawnee Boy, Augusta Stevenson. Trade and School Editions, Bobbs-Merrill.

We Were There with the Mayflower Pilgrims, Robert Webb. Grosset.

INTERESTING WORDS IN THIS BOOK

astonishment (ăs tŏn′ĭsh mĕnt) : amazement; surprise

attempt (ă tĕmpt′) : try

baptize (băp tīz') : to sprinkle water upon one's head, in a religious rite

billowing (bĭl'ō ĭng) : moving, like waves

chinquapin (chĭng'kȧ pĭn) : nut from the dwarf chestnut tree; the tree itself

circlet (sûr'klĕt) : a little circle, as a ring, bracelet, or headband

commoner (kŏm'ŭn ẽr) : one of the common people; not of the nobility

disappear (dĭs ȧ pēr') : to go out of sight

dwindle (dwĭn'd'l) : to become fewer

explore (ĕks plōr') : to seek something new

flaw (flô) : a weak or faulty part

gesture (jĕs'tŭr) : motion of the body or limbs to explain something or enforce an argument

gleefully (glē'fŏŏl lĭ) : merrily; gaily

image (ĭm'ĭj) : likeness; copy

imploring (ĭm plōr'ĭng) : pleading

imprisoned (ĭm prĭz''nd) : enclosed

insist (ĭn sĭst') : to take a stand and not give way; to urge

intend (ĭn tĕnd') : to plan

jagged (jăg′ĕd) : sharply pointed

linger (lĭng′gẽr) : to be slow in leaving

mantle (măn′t′l) : loose sleeveless garment worn over other garments; a cloak

mask (måsk) : a festive dance where all wear masks

molest (mȯ lĕst′) : to bother so as to injure

persimmon (pẽr sĭm′ŭn) : plumlike fruit, sweet and tasty when ripe

prickly (prĭk′lĭ) : sharp; spiny

protest (prō tĕst′) : object to

quiver (kwĭv′ẽr) : case for carrying arrows

rector (rĕk′tẽr) : preacher

reflection (rė̇ flĕk′shŭn) : image given back by a mirror

reproof (rė̇ prōof′) : blame for a fault or misdeed

sentry (sĕn′trĭ) : a guard

stalk (stôk) : to follow silently

stockade (stŏk ād′) : enclosure or pen made of posts and stakes

succotash (sŭk′ȯ tăsh) : beans and corn cooked together

suspect (sŭs pĕkt′) : imagine something to be true

wield (wēld) : to handle with skill